بسم الله الرحمن الرحيم

ABOUT THE AUTHOR

The author, who writes under the pen-name HARUN YAHYA, was born in Ankara in 1956. Having completed his primary and secondary education in Ankara, he then studied arts at Istanbul's Mimar Sinan University and philosophy at Istanbul University. Since the 1980s, the author has published many books on political, faith-related and scientific issues. Harun Yahya is well-known as an author who has written very important works disclosing the imposture of evolutionists, the invalidity of their claims and the dark liaisons between Darwinism and bloody ideologies such as fascism and communism.

His pen-name is made up of the names "Harun" (Aaron) and "Yahya" (John), in memory of the two esteemed prophets who fought against lack of faith. The Prophet's seal on the cover of the author's books has a symbolic meaning linked to the their contents. This seal represents the Qur'an, the last Book and the last word of God, and our Prophet, the last of all the prophets. Under the guidance of the Qur'an and Sunnah, the author makes it his main goal to disprove each one of the fundamental tenets of godless ideologies and to have the "last word", so as to completely silence the objections raised against religion. The seal of the Prophet, who attained ultimate wisdom and moral perfection, is used as a sign of his intention of saying this last word.

All these works by the author centre around one goal: to convey the message of the Qur'an to people, thus encouraging them to think about basic faith-related issues, such as the existence of God, His unity and the hereafter, and to display the decrepit foundations and perverted works of godless systems.

Harun Yahya enjoys a wide readership in many countries, from India to America, England to Indonesia, Poland to Bosnia, and Spain to Brazil. Some of his books are available in English, French, German, Italian, Spanish, Portuguese, Urdu, Arabic, Albanian, Russian, Serbo-Croat (Bosnian), Polish, Malay, Uygur Turkish, and Indonesian, and they have been enjoyed by readers all over the world.

Greatly appreciated all around the world, these works have been instrumental in many people putting their faith in God and in many others gaining a deeper insight into their faith. The wisdom, and the sincere and easy-to-understand style employed give these books a distinct touch which directly strikes any one who reads or examines them. Immune to objections, these works are characterised by their features of rapid effectiveness, definite results and irrefutability. It is unlikely that those who read these books and give a serious thought to them can any longer sincerely advocate the materialistic philosophy, atheism and any other perverted ideology or philosophy. Even if they continue to advocate, this will be only a sentimental insistence since these books have refuted these ideologies from their very basis. All contemporary movements of denial are ideologically defeated today, thanks to the collection of books written by Harun Yahya.

There is no doubt that these features result from the wisdom and lucidity of the Qur'an. The author certainly does not feel proud of himself; he merely intends to serve as a means in one's search for God's right path. Furthermore, no material gain is sought in the publication of these works.

Considering these facts, those who encourage people to read these books, which open the "eyes" of the heart and guide them in becoming more devoted servants of God, render an invaluable service.

Meanwhile, it would just be a waste of time and energy to propagate other books which create confusion in peoples' minds, lead man into ideological chaos, and which, clearly have no strong and precise effects in removing the doubts in peoples' hearts, as also verified from previous experience. It is apparent that it is impossible for books devised to emphasize the author's literary power rather than the noble goal of saving people from loss of faith, to have such a great effect. Those who doubt this can readily see that the sole aim of Harun Yahya's books is to overcome disbelief and to disseminate the moral values of the Qur'an. The success, impact and sincerity this service has attained are manifest in the reader's conviction.

One point needs to be kept in mind: The main reason for the continuing cruelty and conflict, and all the ordeals the majority of people undergo is the ideological prevalence of disbelief. These things can only come to an end with the ideological defeat of disbelief and by ensuring that everybody knows about the wonders of creation and Qur'anic morality, so that people can live by it. Considering the state of the world today, which forces people into the downward spiral of violence, corruption and conflict, it is clear that this service has to be provided more speedily and effectively. Otherwise, it may be too late.

It is no exaggeration to say that the collection of books by Harun Yahya have assumed this leading role. By the Will of God, these books will be the means through which people in the 21st century will attain the peace and bliss, justice and happiness promised in the Qur'an.

THE
MIRACLE
IN THE
ATOM

To Him is due the primal origin of the heavens
and the earth. When He decides on something,
He just says to it, 'Be!' and it is.
(Surat al-Baqara: 117)

HARUN YAHYA

Ta-Ha Publishers Ltd.
I Wynne Road London SW9 0BB

TO THE READER

In all the books by the author, faith-related issues are explained in the light of the Qur'anic verses and people are invited to learn God's words and to live by them. All the subjects that concern God's verses are explained in such a way as to leave no room for doubt or question marks in the reader's mind. The sincere, plain and fluent style employed ensures that everyone of every age and from every social group can easily understand the books. This effective and lucid narrative makes it possible to read them in a single sitting. Even those who rigorously reject spirituality are influenced by the facts recounted in these books and cannot refute the truthfulness of their contents.

This book and all the other works of the author can be read individually or discussed in a group at a time of conversation. Those readers who are willing to profit from the books will find discussion very useful in the sense that they will be able to relate their own reflections and experiences to one another.

In addition, it will be a great service to the religion to contribute to the presentation and reading of these books, which are written solely for the good pleasure of God. All the books of the author are extremely convincing. For this reason, for those who want to communicate the religion to other people, one of the most effective methods is to encourage them to read these books.

It is hoped that the reader will take time to look through the review of other books on the final pages of the book, and appreciate the rich source of material on faith-related issues, which are very useful and a pleasure to read.

In these books, you will not find, as in some other books, the personal views of the author, explanations based on dubious sources, styles that are unobservant of the respect and reverence due to sacred subjects, nor hopeless, doubt-creating, and pessimistic accounts that create deviations in the heart.

CONTENTS

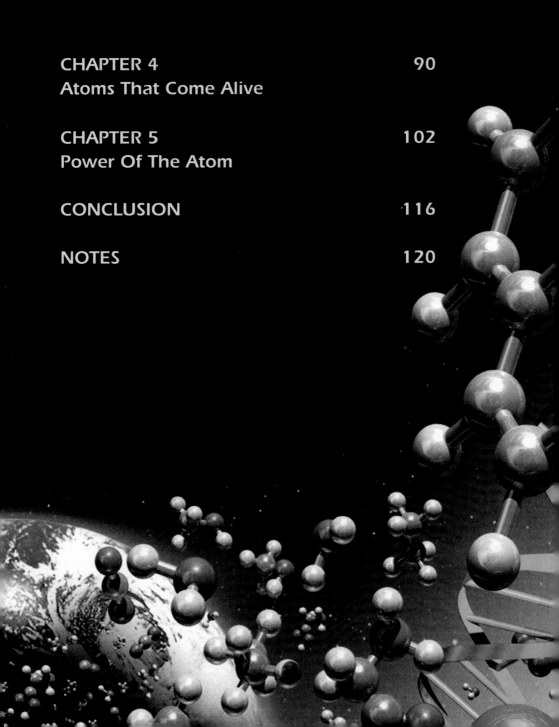

INTRODUCTION

"Why?"

Once the answer is found, this question is the key to a gate that leads one to a completely different world. It is, at the same time, a slim line that separates those who know from those who don't.

In the world in which we live, mankind is caught up in a continuous search for the answers to many questions like "what?", "how?" and "in what way?", and can make but little headway in answering them. It is unlikely for man to make his way to the truth unless he asks himself the question "why?" about the extraordinary order and balance with which he interacts.

In this book, we will deal with the subject of "the atom", the groundwork of every animate and inanimate thing. After seeing what occurs and in what way it occurs with regards to the atom, we will seek the answers to the question "why?" The answer to this question will take us to the truth we pursue. We will find the answers to this question in the Qur'an, the divine guide that contains the explanation for everything.

Since the first half of the 19th century, hundreds of scientists worked day and night to reveal the secrets of the atom. These studies that uncovered the form, motion, structure and other properties of the atom shattered the very grounds of classical physics that assumed matter to be an entity without any beginning or end, and laid the foundation for modern physics. They also produced many questions.

Many physicists, looking for answers to these questions, finally agreed that there is perfect order, unerring balance and conscious design in the atom, as in everything else in the universe.

This truth is revealed in the Qur'an sent down by Allah fourteen centuries ago. As made clear in the verses of the Qur'an, the whole universe works in perfect order because the earth, the sky and everything in between is cre-

ated by Allah, Who has infinite power and wisdom.

It is certainly no wonder that everything created by Allah has extraordinary excellence and runs within a flawless order. What comes as a real surprise is man's unrelenting insensitivity towards the numerous miracles he encounters, sees, hears, and knows – including his own body – and his negligence about the reason "why" these extraordinary details are presented to him.

Though dwelling on a scientific subject, the purpose of *"The Miracle in the Atom"* is different from that of conventional scientific books. This book deals with the "atom", unique in being the building block of both animate and inanimate objects, with the questions "what?", "how?" and "in what way?", thereby opening the door to the answer of the question "why?" Once beyond this door, the superiority of the wisdom and knowledge of Allah, and His creation will be revealed for all to see:

> **Allah, there is no god but Him, the Living, the Self-Sustaining. He is not subject to drowsiness or sleep. Everything in the heavens and the earth belongs to Him. Who can intercede with Him except by His permission? He knows what is before them and what is behind them but they cannot grasp any of His knowledge save what He wills. His Footstool encompasses the heavens and the earth and their preservation does not tire Him. (Surat al-Baqara: 255)**

CHAPTER 1

THE FORMATION ADVENTURE OF THE ATOM

The universe, whose vast dimension pushes the limits of the human's comprehension, functions without fail, resting on sensitive balances and within a great order and has done so since the first moment of its formation. How this enormous universe has come into being, where it leads to and how the laws that maintain the order and balance within it work, have always been matters of interest to people in all ages, and still are. Scientists made countless researches into these subjects and produced various arguments and theories. For scientists who measured the order and design in the universe by using their reason and conscience, it has not been difficult at all to explain this perfection. This is because Allah, the Almighty, Who rules over the entire universe, created this perfect design and this is obvious and clear to all people who can think and reason. Allah proclaims this evident truth in the verses of the Qur'an:

In the creation of the heavens and the earth, and the alternation of night and day, there are Signs for people with intelligence. (Surat Al 'Imran: 190)

Those scientists who ignore the evidence of creation, however, have great difficulty in answering these never-ending questions. They do not hesitate to take recourse to demagoguery, false theories without any scientific basis, and, if forced into a corner, even deceptions to defend theories that are entirely opposed to reality. Yet, all developments that have taken place in science recently, up until the outset of the 21st century, lead us to a single fact: the universe was created from nothing by Allah, Who possesses superior might and infinite wisdom.

The Creation of the Universe

For centuries, people searched for an answer to the question of "how the universe came into being". Thousands of models of the universe have been put forward and thousands of theories have been produced throughout history. However, a review of these theories reveals that they all have at their core one of two different models. The first is the concept of an infinite universe without beginning, which no longer has any scientific basis. The second is that the universe was created from nothing, which is currently recognized by the scientific community as "the standard model".

11

The first model, which has proven not to be viable, defended the proposition that the universe has existed for an infinite time and will exist endlessly in its current state. This idea of an infinite universe was developed in ancient Greece, and made its way to the western world as a product of the materialistic philosophy that was revived with Renaissance. At the core of the Renaissance lay a re-examination of the works of ancient Greek thinkers. Thus, materialist philosophy and the concept of an infinite universe defended by this philosophy were taken off the dusty shelves of history by philosophical and ideological concerns and presented to people as if they were scientific facts.

Materialists like Karl Marx and Friedrich Engels vigorously embraced this idea, which prepared an apparently solid ground for their materialist ideologies, thereby playing an important role in introducing this model to the 20th century.

According to this "infinite universe" model which was popular during the first half of the 20th century, the universe had no beginning or end. The universe had not been created from nothing, nor would it ever be destroyed. According to this theory, which also laid the basis for materialist philosophy, the universe had a static structure. Yet, later scientific findings revealed that this theory is totally wrong and unscientific. The universe has not existed without beginning; it had a beginning and was created from nothing.

The idea that the universe is infinite, that is that it had no beginning, has always been the starting point of irreligiousness and ideologies that make the mistake of denying Allah. This is because in their view, if the universe had no beginning, then there was no creator either. Yet, science soon revealed with conclusive evidence that these arguments of the materialists are invalid and that the universe started with an explosion called the Big Bang. Coming into being from nothing had only one meaning: "Creation". Allah, the Almighty created the whole universe.

The renowned British astronomer Sir Fred Hoyle was among those who were disturbed by this fact. With his "steady-state" theory, Hoyle accepted that the universe was expanding and argued that the universe was infinite in scale and without beginning or end. According

Sir Fred Hoyle

12

to this model, as the universe expanded, matter originated spontaneously and in quantities as large as required. This theory, which was based on extremely unworkable premises, and advanced by the sole concern of supporting the idea of an "infinite universe without beginning or end" was in direct opposition to the Big Bang theory, which was scientifically proven closer to a great number of observations. Hoyle and others continued to resist this but all scientific development worked against them.

The Expansion of the Universe and the Big Bang

In the 20th century, great strides were made in the field of astronomy. First, the Russian physicist Alexandre Friedmann discovered in 1922 that the universe did not have a static structure. Starting out from Einstein's theory of relativity, Friedmann calculated that even a tiny impulse might cause the universe to expand or contract. Georges Lemaître, one of the most famous astronomers of Belgium, was the first to recognise the importance of this calculation. These calculations led him to conclude that the universe had a beginning and that it was continuously expanding right from the outset. There was another very important point Lemaître raised: according to him, there should be a radiation surplus left over

The universe came into existence out of nothing with a Big Bang. The present perfect system of the universe came about because of the scattering of all particles and forces that were formed in great harmony and order from the first moment of this big explosion.

from the big bang and this could be traced. Lemaître was confident that his explanations were true although they initially did not find much support in the scientific community. Meanwhile, further evidence that the universe was expanding began to pile up. At that time, observing a number of stars through his huge telescope, the American astronomer Edwin Hubble discovered that the stars emitted a red shifted light depending on their distances.

Georges Lemaître

With this discovery, which he made at the California Mount Wilson Observatory, Hubble challenged all scientists who put forward and defended the steady state theory, and shook the very basis of the model of the universe held until then.

Hubble's findings depended on the physical rule that the spectra of light beams travelling towards the point of observation tend towards violet while the spectra of light beams moving away from the point of observation tend towards red. This showed that the celestial bodies observed from the Californian Mount Wilson Observatory were moving away from the earth. Further observation revealed that the stars and galaxies weren't just racing away from us; they were racing away from each other as well. This movement of celestial bodies proved once more that the universe is expanding. In *Stephen Hawking's Universe*, David Filkin relates an interesting point about these developments:

...Within two years, Lemaître heard the news

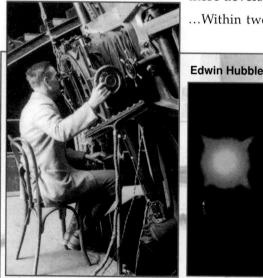

Edwin Hubble

The analysis of the light of the two stars of Alpha Centauri over a period of time showed a series of changes in their spectra. The way the red and blue shifts vary revealed a picture of two stars completing orbits around each other once every 80 years.

he had scarcely dared hope for. Hubble had observed that the light from galaxies was red shifted, and, according to Doppler effect, this had to mean the universe was expanding. Now it was only a matter of time. Einstein was interested in Hubble's work anyway and resolved to visit him at the Mount Wilson Observatory. Lemaître arranged to give a lecture at the California Institute of Technology at the same time, and managed to corner Einstein and Hubble together. He argued his "primeval atom" theory carefully, step by step, suggesting that the whole universe had been created "on a day which had no yesterday." Painstakingly he worked through all the mathematics. When he had finished he could not believe his ears. Einstein stood up and announced that what he had just heard was "the most beautiful and satisfying interpretation I have listened to" and went on to confess that creating the "cosmological constant" was "the biggest blunder" of his life.[1]

The truth that made Einstein, who is considered one of the most important scientists in history, jump to his feet was the fact that the universe has a beginning.

Albert Einstein, during a visit to the Wilson Observatory, where Edwin Hubble made his observations.

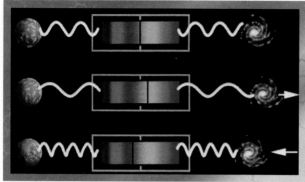

According to the Doppler effect, if a galaxy stays at a constant distance from the earth, the spectra of light waves will appear in the "standard" position (top). If the galaxy is moving away from us, the waves will seem stretched and red shifted (middle). If the galaxy is moving towards us, the waves will seem squashed up and blue shifted (bottom).

Further observations on the expansion of the universe gave way to new arguments. Starting from this point, scientists ended up with a model of a universe that became smaller as one went back in time, eventually contracting and converging at a single point, as Lemaître had argued. The conclusion to be derived from this model is that at some point in time, all matter in the universe was crushed together in a single point-mass that had "zero volume" because of its immense gravitational force. Our universe came into being as the result of the explosion of this point-mass that had zero volume and this explosion has come to be called the "Big Bang".

The Big Bang pointed to another matter. To say that something has zero volume is tantamount to saying that it is "nothing". The whole universe is created from this "nothing". Furthermore, this universe has a beginning, contrary to the view of materialism, which holds that "the universe has existed from eternity".

Big Bang with Evidence

Once the fact that the universe started to form after a great explosion was established, astrophysicists gave a further boost to their researches. According to George Gamow, if the universe was formed in a sudden, cataclysmic explosion, there ought to be a definite amount of radiation left over from that explosion which should be uniform throughout the universe.

In the years following this hypothesis, scientific findings followed one another, all confirming the Big Bang. In

George Gamow

16

The gigantic horn antenna at Bell Laboratories where Arno Penzias and Robert Wilson discovered the cosmic background radiation. Penzias and Wilson were awarded the Nobel Prize for this discovery in 1978.

1965, two researchers by the name of Arno Penzias and Robert Wilson chanced upon a form of radiation hitherto unnoticed. Called "cosmic background radiation", it was unlike anything coming from anywhere else in the universe for it was extraordinarily uniform. It was neither localised nor did it have a definite source; instead, it was distributed equally everywhere. It was soon realised that this radiation is the relic of the Big Bang, still reverberating since the first moments of that great explosion. Gamow had been spot-on, for the frequency of the radiation was nearly the same value that scientists had predicted. Penzias and Wilson were awarded the Nobel Prize for their discovery.

It took only eight minutes for George Smoot and his NASA team to confirm the levels of radiation reported by Penzias and Wilson, thanks to the COBE space satellite. The sensitive sensors on board the satellite earned a new victory for the Big Bang theory. The sensors verified the existence of the hot, dense form remaining from the first moments of the Big Bang. COBE captured evidentiary remnants of the Big Bang, and the scientific community was compelled to acknowledge it.

Other evidence had to do with the relative amounts of hydrogen and helium in the universe. Calculations revealed that the proportion of hydrogen-helium gasses in the universe is in accord with theoretical calculations of what should remain after the Big Bang.

George Smoot

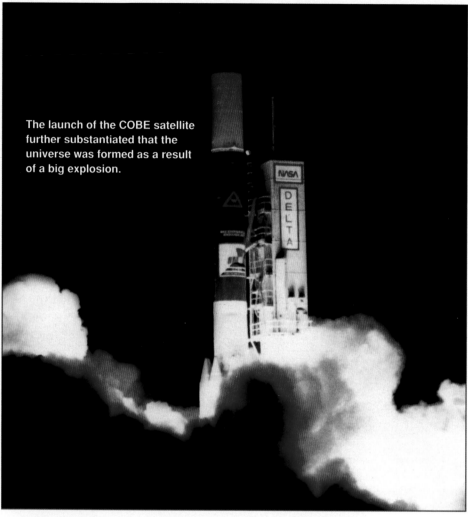

The launch of the COBE satellite further substantiated that the universe was formed as a result of a big explosion.

The discovery of compelling evidence caused the Big Bang theory to gain the complete approval of the scientific world. In an article in its October 1994 issue, *Scientific American* noted that "the Big Bang model was the only acknowledged model of the 20th century"

Confessions were forthcoming one by one from the names who had defended the "infinite universe" concept for years. Defending the steady-state theory alongside Fred Hoyle for years, Dennis Sciama described the final position they had reached after all the evidence for the Big Bang theory was revealed:

There was at that time a somewhat acrimonious debate between some of the proponents of the steady state theory and observers who were testing it and, I think, hoping to disprove it. I played a very minor part at that time because I was a supporter of the steady state theory, not in the sense that I believed that it had to be true, but in that I found it so attractive I wanted it to be true. When hostile observational evidence became to come in, Fred Hoyle took a leading part in trying to counter this evidence, and I played a small part at the side, also making suggestions as to how the hostile evidence could be answered. But as that evidence piled up, it became more and more evident that the game was up, and that one had to abandon the steady state theory.[2]

Allah Created the Universe from Nothing

With ample evidence discovered by science, the thesis of an "infinite universe" was tossed onto the scrap-heap of the history of scientific ideas. Yet, more important questions were forthcoming: what existed before the Big Bang? What force could have caused the great explosion that resulted in a universe that did not exist before?

There is a single answer to be given to the question of what existed before the Big Bang: Allah, the All-powerful and the Almighty, Who created the earth and the heavens in great order. Many scientists, be they believers or not, are obliged to admit this truth. Although they may decline to admit this fact on scientific platforms, their confessions in between the lines give them away. Renowned atheist philosopher Anthony Flew says:

Notoriously, confession is good for the soul. I will therefore begin by confessing that **the Stratonician atheist has to be embarrassed by the contemporary cosmological consensus.** For it seems that the cosmologists are providing a scientific proof of what St. Thomas contended could not be proved philosophically; namely, that the universe had a beginning. So long as the universe can be comfortably thought of as being not only without end but also beginning, it remains easy to urge that its brute existence, and whatever are found to be its most fundamental features, should be accepted as the explanatory ultimates. Although I believe that it

remains still correct, it certainly is neither easy nor comfortable to maintain this position in the face of the Big Bang story.[3]

Some scientists like the British materialist physicist H. P. Lipson confess that they have to accept the Big Bang theory whether they want it or not:

> If living matter is not, then, caused by the interplay of atoms, natural forces, and radiation, how has it come into being?... I think, however, that **we must...admit that the only acceptable explanation is creation**. I know that this is anathema to physicists, as indeed it is to me, but we must not reject that we do not like if the experimental evidence supports it.[4]

In conclusion, science points to a single reality whether materialist scientists like it or not. Matter and time have been created by a Creator, Who is All-Powerful and Who created the heavens, the earth and all that is in between: Almighty Allah.

> **It is Allah who created the seven heavens and of the earth the same number, the Command descending down through all of them, so that you might know that Allah has power over all things and that Allah encompasses all things in His knowledge. (Surat at-Talaq: 12)**

The Signs of the Qur'an

In addition to explaining the universe, the Big Bang model has another important implication. As the quotation from Anthony Flew cited above points out, science has proven an assertion hitherto supported only by religious sources.

The truth that is defended by religious sources is the reality of creation from nothingness. This has been declared in the scriptures that have served as guides for mankind for thousands of years. In all scriptures such as the

Old Testament, New Testament, and the Qur'an, it is declared that the universe and everything in it were created from nothingness by Allah.

In the only book revealed by Allah that has survived completely intact, the Qur'an, there are statements about the creation of the universe from nothing as well as how this came about that are suggestive of 20th-century ideas and yet were revealed fourteen centuries ago.

First of all, the creation of this universe from nothingness is revealed in the Qur'an as follows:

He (Allah) is the Originator of the heavens and the earth... (Surat al-An'am: 101)

Another important point revealed in the Qur'an fourteen centuries before the modern discovery of the Big Bang and findings related to it is that when it was created, the universe occupied a very tiny volume:

Do those who are disbelievers not see that the heavens and the earth were sewn together and then We unstitched them and that We made from water every living thing? So will they not have faith? (Surat al-Anbiya': 30)

There is a very important choice of words in the original Arabic whose translation is given above. The word *ratq* translated as **"sewn to"** means "mixed in each, blended" in Arabic dictionaries. It is used to refer to two different substances that make up a whole. The phrase **"We unstitched"** is the verb *fataqa* in Arabic and implies that something comes into being by tearing apart or destroying the structure of *ratq*. The sprouting of a seed from the soil is one of the actions to which this verb is applied.

Let us take a look at the verse again with this knowledge in mind. In the verse, sky and earth are at first subject in the condition of *ratq*. They are separated (*fataqa*) with one coming out of the other. Intriguingly, cosmologists speak of a "cosmic egg" that consisted of all the matter in the universe prior to the Big Bang. In other words, all the heavens and earth were included in this egg in a condition of *ratq*. This cosmic egg exploded violently causing its matter to *fataqa* and in the process created the structure of the whole universe.

Another matter in the Qur'an that could be interpreted as the expansion of the universe, which was discovered in the late 1920s. Hubble's discovery of the red shift in the spectrum of starlight is revealed in the Qur'an as :

It is We Who have built the universe with (Our creative) power, and, verily, it is We Who are steadily expanding it. (Surat adh-Dhariyat: 47)

In short, the findings of modern science increasingly point towards the truth that is revealed in the Qur'an and do not support materialist dogma. Materialists may claim this all as "coincidence" but the plain fact is that the universe came into being as a result of an act of creation on the part of Allah. The only true knowledge about the origin of universe is to be found in the word of Allah as revealed to us.

Creation of Matter Moment by Moment

As the Big Bang theory showed once more, Allah created the universe from nothing. This great explosion involves many fine gradations and details, prodding one to reflection, and these matters unaccountable for by coincidence.

The temperature at each moment of the explosion, the number of atomic particles, the forces involved, and their intensity must be of very precise values. Even if only one of these values was not specified, the universe we live in today would not be formed. This end would be inevitable if any one of the abovementioned values deviated by any value mathematically close to "0".

In short, the universe and its building blocks, the atoms, have come to exist in the immediate aftermath of the Big Bang after having not existed, thanks to these balances created by Allah. Scientists conducted numerous researches to understand the chronology of the events that took place during this process and the order of the rules of physics in effect at each phase. The facts all scientists who have worked on this subject today admit are as follows:

◆ Moment "0": This "moment" when matter and time were non-existent, and when the explosion took place is accepted as t (time) = 0 in physics. This means that nothing exists at time t=0. In order to be able to describe earlier than this "moment" when creation was initiated, we must know the rules of physics that existed then, because the current laws of physics do not count for the first moments of the explosion.

The events that may be defined by physics start at 10^{-43} seconds, which is the smallest time unit. This is a time frame incomprehensible to the human mind. What happened in this small time period of which we cannot even conceive? Physicists have hitherto been unable to develop a theory that explains in full detail the events that took place at that moment.[5]

This is because scientists do not have the data required to make the calculations. The scope of the rules of mathematics and physics is at a dead-end at these limits. That is, both what went before and what happened at the first moments of this explosion, every detail of which rests on highly delicate balances, have a reality beyond the confines of the human mind and physics.

This creation, which started at before time, has led moment by moment to the formation of the material universe and the laws of physics. Now let us take a look at the incidents that occurred with great precision within a very short time during this explosion.

As mentioned above, in physics, everything can be calculated from 10^{-43} seconds onwards, and energy and time can be defined only after this moment. At this point of the creation, the temperature is 10^{32} (100,000,000,000,000,000,000,000,000,000,000) K. To draw a comparison, the temperature of the sun is expressed in millions (10^8) and the temperature of some stars much larger than the sun is expressed in billions (10^{11}). That the highest measurable temperature at present is limited to billions of degrees reveals how high the temperature was at 10^{-43} seconds.

◆ When we go one step further than this period of 10^{-43} seconds, we come to the point at which time is at 10^{-37} seconds. The time lapse between these two periods is not something like one or two seconds. We are talking about a time lapse as short as one over quadrillion times quadrillion of a second. The temperature is still extraordinarily high, at 10^{29} (100,000,000,000,000,000,000,000,000,000) K. No atoms were yet created at this stage.[6]

◆ One more step, and we are at 10^{-2} seconds. This time period indicates one hundredth of a second. By now, the temperature is 100 billion degrees. At this point, the "early universe" has started to form. Particles like the proton and neutron forming the nucleus of the atom have not yet appeared. There is only the electron and its antiparticle, the positron (anti-electron), because the temperature and speed of the universe at that point only allow the formation of these particles. In less than a second after the explosion has taken place out of nothing, electrons and positrons have formed.

From this moment on, the time of the formation of each sub-atomic particle is very important. Every particle has to emerge at a specific moment so that the current rules of physics may be established. It is of great importance which particle is to form first. Even a slight deviation in the sequence or timing would make it impossible for the universe to take its current shape.

Let us stop now and do some thinking.

The Big Bang theory provides evidence for Allah's being by showing that all matter comprising the universe originated from nothingness. It did even more and showed that the building blocks – the atoms – also came into existence from nothing less than one second after the Big

3 MINUTES
Protons and neutron form atomic nuclei.

Following moment "0" when no matter or time existed and when the explosion occurred, the universe, and its building blocks, the atoms, were created out of nothing within a great scheme.

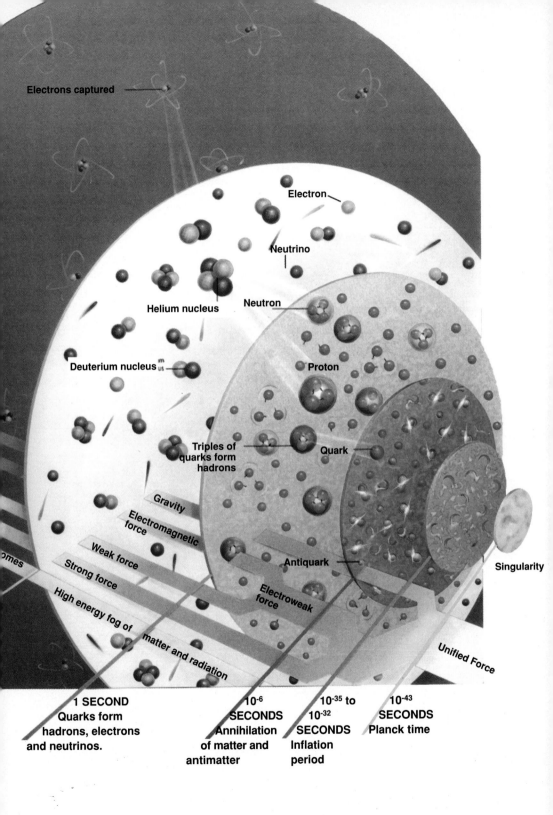

Electrons captured

Electron

Neutrino

Helium nucleus

Neutron

Deuterium nucleus

Proton

Triples of quarks form hadrons

Quark

Gravity

Electromagnetic force

Weak force

Strong force

Antiquark

High energy fog of matter and radiation

Electroweak force

omes

Singularity

Unified Force

1 SECOND
Quarks form
hadrons, electrons
and neutrinos.

10^{-6}
SECONDS
Annihilation
of matter and
antimatter

10^{-35} to
10^{-32}
SECONDS
Inflation
period

10^{-43}
SECONDS
Planck time

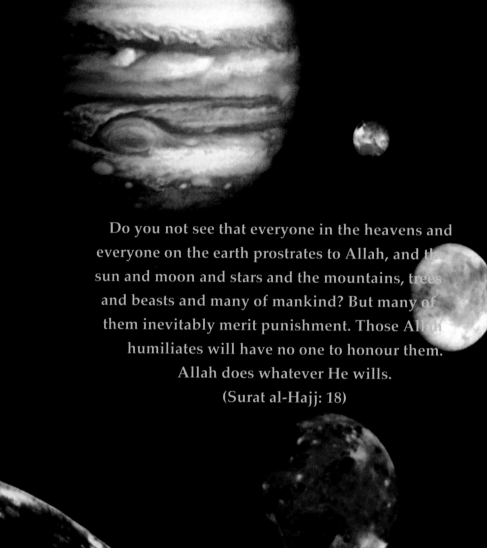

Do you not see that everyone in the heavens and everyone on the earth prostrates to Allah, and the sun and moon and stars and the mountains, trees and beasts and many of mankind? But many of them inevitably merit punishment. Those Allah humiliates will have no one to honour them. Allah does whatever He wills.

(Surat al-Hajj: 18)

Bang. The enormous equilibrium and order in these particles are worthy of note. The universe owes its present state to this equilibrium that will be described in more detail in the pages ahead. It is again this equilibrium that allows us to live a peaceful life. In short, perfect order and un-changing laws, "the laws of physics", have formed following an explosion that would normally be expected to create great turmoil and disorder. This proves that each moment following the creation of the universe, including the Big Bang, has been designed perfectly.

Now, let us continue looking at the developments from where we left off.

◆ The next step is the moment at which a time of 10^{-1} seconds has elapsed. At this moment, the temperature is 30 billion degrees. Not even one second has elapsed from $t = 0$ moment to this stage. By now, neutrons and protons, the other particles of the atom, have started to appear. The neutrons and protons, the perfect structures of which we will analyse in the following sections, were created out of nothing within a time period even shorter than a second.

◆ Let us come to the first second after the explosion. The massive density at this time again gives a colossal figure. According to calculations, the density value of the mass present at that stage is 3.8 billion kilograms per litre. It may be easy to express this figure, termed as billions of kilograms, arithmetically, and to show it on paper. Yet, it is impossible to conceive of this figure exactly. To give a very simple example to express the magnitude of this figure, we can say "if Mount Everest in the Himalayas had this density, it could swallow our world in a moment with the force of gravitation it would possess."[7]

◆ The most distinctive characteristic of the subsequent moments is that by then, the temperature has reached a considerably lower level. At that stage, the universe is approximately 14 seconds old, has a temperature of 3 billion degrees and continues to expand at a dramatic speed.

This is the stage where the steady atomic nuclei, like hydrogen and helium nuclei, have started to form. One proton and one neutron have for the first time found conditions conducive to their co-existing. These two particles, which have a mass straddling the line between existence and non-existence, have, because of the force of gravitation, started resisting the tremendous rate of expansion. It is obvious that a dramatically conscious and controlled process is in progress here. A massive explosion gives way to great equilibrium and precise order. Protons and neutrons have started to come together to form the atom, the building block of matter. It is certainly totally impossible for these particles to have the power and consciousness to establish the delicate balances required for the formation of matter.

◆ During the epoch following this formation, the temperature of the universe has dropped to one billion degrees. This temperature is 60 times the temperature at the core of our sun. Only 3 minutes and 2 seconds have elapsed from the first instant to this one. By now, sub-atomic particles like photons, protons, anti protons, neutrinos and anti-neutrinos are abundant. The quantities of all the particles existing in this phase and their interactions with each other are extremely critical. So much so that the slightest variation in the quantity of any particle will destroy the energy level set by them and prevent the conversion of energy into matter.

Take electrons and positrons for example: when electrons and positrons come together, energy is produced. Therefore, the numbers of both particles are very important. Let us say that 10 units of electrons and 8 units of positrons meet. In this case, 8 of the 10 units of electrons interact with 8 units of positrons and produce energy. As a result, 2 units of electrons are released. Since the electron is one of the particles forming the atom that is the building block of the universe, it has to be available in required quantities in this stage so that the universe may exist. To take up the abovementioned example, if the number of positrons was more than that of the electrons, then positrons would be left over instead of electrons as a result of the energy released and the material universe would never be formed. If the numbers of positrons and electrons were equal, then only energy would be produced and nothing left to form the material universe. Yet, this excess in the number of electrons has been arranged in such a way as to match the number of protons in the universe in the time that follows this moment. In the atom that will form later on, the numbers of electrons and protons will be equal.

The numbers of particles that emerged in the aftermath

Steven Weinberg of the Big Bang were determined with so precise a calculati-

on, finally leading to the formation of
the material universe. Professor Steven
Weinberg remarks on how critical is the
interaction between these particles:

The Hydrogen Atom

> If the universe in the first few minutes was
> really composed of precisely equal num-
> bers of particles and antiparticles, they wo-
> uld all have annihilated as the temperature
> dropped below 1,000 million degrees, and not-
> hing would be left but radiation. There is a very
> good evidence against this possibility – we are
> here! There must have been some excess of
> electrons over positrons, of protons over an-
> tiprotons, and of neutrons over antineut-
> rons, in order that there would be somet-
> hing left over after the annihilation of particles
> and antiparticles to furnish the matter of the present universe.[8]

The Helium Atom

◆ A total of 34 minutes and 40 seconds have passed since the outset.
Our universe is now half an hour old. The temperature has dropped from
degrees expressed in billions to 300 million degrees. The electrons and positrons continue producing energy by colliding with each other. By now, the
quantities of the particles that are to form the universe have been balanced to
allow the formation of the material universe.

Once the rate of the explosion slows down, these particles, almost lac-
king a mass, start to interact with one another. The first hydrogen atom
forms by an electron settling into the orbit of a proton. This formation introduces us to the fundamental forces we will commonly encounter in the universe.

It is no doubt impossible for these particles, which are products of a design far beyond human comprehension and have distinct structures resting
on extremely delicate balances, to have come together through coincidence
and to act towards the same goal. This perfection leads many researchers
working on the subject to a very important conclusion: it is a "creation" and
there is a matchless supervision of every moment of this creation. Each particle that is created after the explosion is supposed to form at a specific time,

at a specific temperature and at a specific velocity. It seems that this system, which runs almost like a wound-up clock, had been programmed with such fine-tuning before becoming active. This means that the Big Bang and the perfect universe that originated as a result of the Big Bang had been designed before the inception of the explosion and afterwards put into action.

The will that arranges, designs and controls the universe is certainly that of Allah, the Creator of everything.

This design is observable not only in the atom, but in every object in the universe, big or small. These particles, which initially dashed away from each other at the speed of light, not only caused the formation of hydrogen atoms, but also gave rise to all the enormous systems contained within the universe today, as well as the atoms, molecules, planets, suns, solar systems, galaxies, quasars etc., according to a magnificent plan, and in perfect order and balance. While it is impossible for the particles required to form an atom to come together by chance and establish delicate balances, it would be far more unreasonable and illogical to claim that planets, galaxies, and in short, all systems that provide the workings of the universe to form by chance and develop balances by themselves. The will that makes this unique design is that of Allah, the Creator of the entire universe.

Other atoms formed following the hydrogen atom, which was a miracle on its own. At this point, various questions come to mind such as "How did other atoms form? Why didn't all protons and neutrons form only the hydrogen atom? How did the particles decide which atoms they would form and in what quantities?" The answer to these questions again takes us to the same conclusion. There is a great power, control and design in the formation of the hydrogen atom and all the other atoms that followed. This control and design exceeds the capacity of the human mind and points to the fact that the universe is obviously a "creation." The laws of physics that were established in the aftermath of the Big Bang have not changed at all during the approximately 17 billion years that have passed. Furthermore, these laws are based on such precise calculations that even millimetric deviations from their present values may cause results upsetting the general structure and order in the entire universe. The words of famous physicist Prof. Stephen Hawking addressing this point are quite interesting. Hawking explains that these phenomena are based on much finer calculations then we can imagine:

> If the rate of expansion one second after the big bang had been smaller by even one part in a hundred thousand million million, the universe would have recollapsed before it ever reached its present size.[9]

> He has made night and day subservient to you, and the sun and moon and stars, all subject to His command. There are certainly Signs in that for people who use their intellect.
> (Surat an-Nahl: 12)

The Big Bang, which is built on such fine calculations, evidently reveals that time, space and matter did not come into being spontaneously, but were created by Allah. It is absolutely impossible for the events described above to have formed as a result of sheer coincidence and to lead to the formation of the atom, the building block of the universe.

Unsurprisingly, many scientists working on the subject have accepted the existence of an infinite force and its might in the creation of the universe. The renowned astrophysicist Hugh Ross explains that the Creator of the universe is beyond all dimensions:

> By definition, time is that dimension in which cause-and-effect phenomena take place. No time, no cause and effect. If time's beginning is concurrent with the beginning of the universe, as the space-time theorem says, then the cause of the universe must be some entity operating in a time dimension completely independent of and pre-existent to the time dimension of the cosmos. ...It tells us that the Creator is transcendent, operating beyond the dimensional limits of the universe. It tells us that God is not the universe itself, nor is God contained within the universe.[10]

The most important aspect of the Big Bang is that it gives mankind the chance to understand Allah's power better. The origination of a universe with all the matter it contains from nothing is one of the greatest signs of Allah's might. The delicate equilibrium in the energy at the moment of the explosion is a very big sign directing us towards thinking about the infinity of Allah's knowledge.

Fundamental Forces In the Universe

We mentioned that the laws of physics in the universe originated after the Big Bang. These laws are based on the "four fundamental forces" known to modern physics today. These forces were formed along with the formation of the first sub-atomic particles at specifically appointed times in the immediate aftermath of the Big Bang to form the entire order and system of the universe. Atoms, which make up the material universe, owe their existence and extremely even distribution across the universe to the interaction of these forces. These forces are the force of mass attraction known as the gravitational force, the electromagnetic force, the strong nuclear force, and the weak nuclear force. All have a distinct intensity and field of impact. The strong and weak nuclear forces operate only at the sub-atomic scale. The remaining two – the gravitational force and the electromagnetic force – govern assemblages of atoms, in other words "matter." The flawless order on the earth is the outcome of the highly delicate proportion of these forces. A comparison of those forces produces a very interesting result. All the matter that was created and dispersed across the universe following the Big Bang was shaped by the effect of these forces, which have wide gulfs between them. Below are the stunningly different values of these forces shown in international standard units:

Strong nuclear force	: 15
Weak nuclear force	: 7.03×10^{-3}
Gravitational force	: 5.90×10^{-39}
Electromagnetic force	: 3.05×10^{-12}

These fundamental forces allow the formation of the material universe through a perfect distribution of power. This proportion between the forces is based on such a delicate balance that they can cause the due effect on particles only at these particular proportions.

1. The Giant Power in the Nucleus: The Strong Nuclear Force

Up to this point, we reviewed how the atom was created moment by moment and the delicate balances acting in this creation. We saw that everything around us, including ourselves, is made up of atoms and these atoms consist of many particles. What then is the force that holds all the particles that form the nucleus of the atom together? This force, which keeps the nucleus intact, and which is the most powerful force defined by the laws of physics, is the "strong nuclear force".

This force ensures that the protons and neutrons in the nucleus of the atom stay together without flying apart. The nucleus of the atom is formed in this way. This force is so strong that it almost causes the protons and neutrons within the nucleus to bind to each other. This is why the minute particles that possess this force are called "gluon" meaning "glue" in Latin. The strength of this bond is adjusted very sensitively. The intensity of this force has been specifically arranged to provide that the protons and neutrons keep at a certain distance to each other. If this force had been just slightly stronger, the protons and the neutrons would bump into each other. If this force had been slightly weaker, they would be dispersed. This force has just the proper degree required for the formation of the nucleus of the atom after the first seconds of the Big Bang.

The Hiroshima and Nagasaki bombings were indicative of how destructive the strong nuclear force becomes once it is liberated. The only reason atomic bombs, which will be reviewed in more detail in the chapters ahead, are so effective is the liberation of tiny amounts of this force hidden in the nucleus of the atom.

2. Safety Belt of the Atom: the Weak Nuclear Force

One of the most important factors maintaining order on the earth is the balance within the atom. This balance ensures that things do not suddenly fall apart or emit harmful radiation. The "weak nuclear force" is responsible for this balance between protons and neutrons in the nucleus of the atom. This force plays an important role in maintaining the equilibrium of the nuclei that contain high numbers of neutrons and protons.

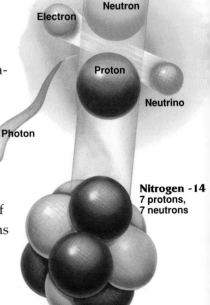

Carbon -14
6 protons
8 neutrons

Neutron

Electron

Proton

Neutrino

Photon

Nitrogen -14
7 protons,
7 neutrons

As this balance is maintained, a neutron, if required, may be changed into a proton. Since the number of protons in the nucleus changes at the end of this process, the atom changes too and becomes a different atom. Here, the result is very significant. An atom transforms into a different atom without disintegrating and continues its existence. This safety belt protects living organisms against the dangers that would otherwise arise from particles breaking free uncontrollably and giving harm to people.

3. The Force That Keeps Electrons in Orbit:
The Electro-magnetic Force

The discovery of this force ushered in a new age in the world of physics. It was then understood that each particle bears "an electrical charge" according to its own structural characteristics and that a force exists between these electrical charges. This force provides that particles with opposite electrical charges attract each other and particles with the same charge repel each other, therefore ensuring that the protons in the nucleus of the atom and the electrons travelling in the orbits around it attract each other. In this way, the "nucleus" and the "electrons", the two basic elements of the atom, stay together.

The slightest change in the strength of this force would cause electrons to shoot away from the nucleus or to fall into the nucleus. In both cases, it would become impossible for the atom and therefore, the material universe to exist. Yet, from the first moment this force formed, the protons in the nucleus attracted the electrons at the exact force required for the formation of the atom thanks to the value of this force.

4. The Force Holding the Universe Together:
The Gravitational Force

Being the only force we can ordinarily perceive, it is also the one about which we know least. Commonly known as gravity, this force is actually called the "mass attraction force". Although it is the least powerful force compared to the other forces, by it very large masses attract each other. This force is the reason why the galaxies and stars in the universe stay in each other's orbits. The earth and other planets remain in a certain orbit around the sun

One can stay in an environment without gravity only for a certain period using special equipment. Living beings can only survive in a system where gravity exists.

Supreme design and perfect order prevail in the entire universe governed by these fundamental forces. The Owner of this order is, beyond doubt, Allah, Who created everything flawlessly out of nothing. Isaac Newton (1642-1727), the father of modern physics and celestial mechanics, who is recognized as "one of the greatest scientists who ever lived" draws attention to this fact:

"This most beautiful system of the sun, planets, and comets could only proceed from the counsel and dominion of an intelligent and powerful Being. This Being governs all things, not as the soul of the world, but as Lord over all, and on account of His dominion. He is wont to be called Lord God, Universal Ruler."

again with the help of this gravitational force. We are able to walk on the earth because of this force. If there were a decline in the value of this force, the stars would fall, the earth would be ripped from its orbit and we would be dispersed from the earth into the space. In the case of the slightest increase, the stars would collide with each other, the earth would run into the sun and we would be pulled into the earth's crust. These may seem very remote possibilities to you now but they would be inevitable if this force had deviated from its present value even for a very short time.

All scientists doing research on this subject admit that the precisely determined values of these fundamental forces are crucial for the existence of the universe.

Addressing this point, the famous molecular biologist Michael Denton states in his book *Nature's Destiny: How the Laws of Biology Reveal Purpose in the Universe*:

If, for example, the gravitational force was a trillion times stronger, then the universe would be far smaller and its life history far shorter. An average star would have a mass a trillion times less than the sun and a life span of about one year. On the other hand, if gravity had been less powerful, no stars or galaxies would have ever formed. The other relationships and values are no less critical. If the strong force had been just slightly weaker, the only element that would be stable would be hydrogen. No other atoms could exist. If it had been slightly stronger in relation to electromagnetism, then an atomic nucleus consisting of only two protons would be a stable feature of the universe-which would mean there would be no hydrogen, and if any stars or galaxies evolved, they would be very different from the way they are. Clearly, if these various forces and constants did not have precisely the values they do, there would be no stars, no supernovae, no planets, no atoms, no life.[11]

Renowned physicist Paul Davies states his admiration for the predetermined values of the laws of physics in the universe:

When one goes on to study cosmology, incredulity mounts. Recent discoveries about the primeval cosmos oblige us to accept that the expanding universe has been set up in its motion with a cooperation of astonishing precision.[12]

Supreme design and perfect order prevail in the entire universe constructed on a foundation provided by these fundamental forces. The owner of this order is, beyond doubt, Allah, Who created everything flawlessly out of nothing. Allah, the Lord of all the worlds, holds the stars in their orbits with the weakest of forces, and holds together the nucleus of the minute atom with the strongest of forces. All forces act according to the "measures" He has determined. Allah refers to the order in the creation of universe and the equilibriums "determined most exactly" in one of His verses:

He to whom the dominion of the heavens and the earth belongs. He does not have a son and He has no partner in His dominion. He created everything and determined it most exactly. (Surat al-Furqan: 2)

CHAPTER 2

THE STRUCTURE OF THE ATOM

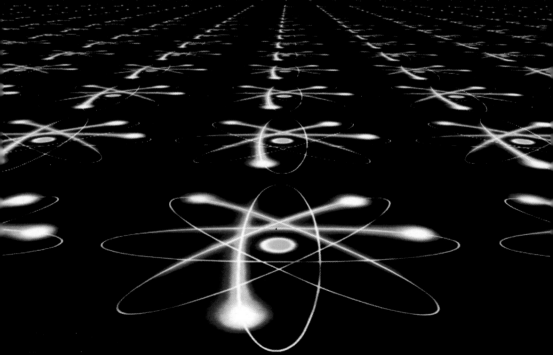

Air, water, mountains, animals, plants, your body, the chair on which you sit, in short, everything you see, touch, and feel, from the heaviest to the lightest is formed of atoms. Each page of the book you hold in your hand comprises billions of atoms. Atoms are particles so minute that it is impossible to view one even with the most powerful microscopes. The diameter of an atom is only of the order of one millionth of a millimetre.

It is not possible for a human being to visualize this size. Therefore, let us try to explain it with an example:

Think that you have a key in your hand. No doubt, it is impossible for you to see the atoms in this key. If you say you must see the atoms, then you have to magnify the key in your hand to the proportions of the world. Once the key in your hand becomes as large as the earth, then each atom inside the key is the size of a cherry.[13]

Let us give another example to comprehend this minuteness and how everywhere and everything is full of atoms:

Let us suppose that we want to count all the atoms in a single grain of salt and let us assume that we are able to count one billion (1,000,000,000) atoms per second. Despite our considerable deftness, we would need over five hundred years to count the number of atoms inside this tiny grain of salt.[14]

What, then, is there inside such a small structure?

Despite its exceedingly small size, there is a flawless, unique and complex system inside the atom comparable in sophistication to the system we see in the universe at large.

Each atom is made up of a nucleus and a number of electrons moving in orbital shells at great distances from the nucleus. Inside the nucleus are other particles called protons and neutrons.

In this chapter, we will look at the extraordinary structure of the atom that constitutes the basis of everything animate and inanimate, and see how the atoms combine to form molecules and ultimately, matter.

Protons and electrons are made up of groups of three quarks.

Atom

The Power Hidden in the Nucleus

The nucleus is located right at the centre of the atom and is made up of a certain number of protons and neutrons depending on the properties of that atom. The radius of the nucleus is about ten thousandth of the radius of the atom. To express that in numbers, the radius of the atom is 10^{-8} (0.00000001) cm, the radius of the nucleus is 10^{-12} (0.000000000001) cm. Therefore, the volume of the nucleus is equal to a ten billionth of the volume of the atom.

Since we cannot visualize this vastness (better to say, minuteness), let us take our example of the cherry. Let us look for the nucleus inside the atoms that we had visualised as the size of cherries when the key in your hand was magnified to be the size of the earth. But such a search would be inconclusive because even at that scale, it is absolutely impossible for us to view the nucleus, which is still exceedingly small. If we really want to see it, then we would have to change the scale again. The cherry representing our atom must again expand and become a large ball two hundred metres in diameter. Even at this unbelievable scale, the nucleus of our atom would not become any bigger than a very tiny grain of dust.[15]

So much so that when we compare the diameter of the nucleus that is 10^{-13} cm and the diameter of the atom that is 10^{-8} cm, we come to the follo-

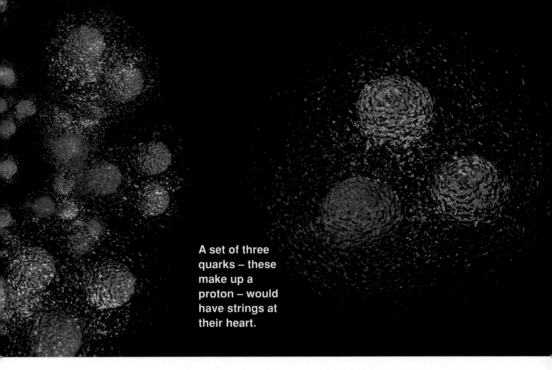

A set of three quarks – these make up a proton – would have strings at their heart.

wing result: if we assume the atom to be a sphere, if we wished to fill this sphere totally with nuclei, then we would need 10^{15} (1,000,000,000,000,000) nuclei to fill it.[16]

Yet there is one thing even more surprising than that: although its size is one ten billionth of an atom's size, the nucleus' mass comprises 99.95% of the mass of the atom. How is it that something constitutes almost all of a given mass, while, on the other hand, occupying almost no space?

The reason is that the density comprising the mass of the atom is not distributed evenly throughout the whole atom. That is, almost the entire mass of the atom is accumulated in the nucleus. Say, you have a house of 10 billion square metres and you have to put all the furniture in the house in a room of one square metre. Can you do this? Of course you cannot. Yet, the atomic nucleus is able to do this thanks to a tremendous force unlike any other force in the universe. This force is the "strong nuclear force", one of the four fundamental forces in the universe we mentioned in the previous chapter.

We had noted that this force, the most powerful of the forces in nature, keeps the nucleus of an atom intact and keeps it from fragmenting. All the protons in the nucleus have positive charges and they repel each other because of the electro-magnetic force. However, due to the strong nuclear force, which is 100 times stronger than the repulsive force of the protons, the elect-ro-magnetic force becomes ineffective, and thus the protons are held toget-her.

To sum up, there are two great forces interacting with each other inside an atom so small as to be unseen to us. The nucleus is able to stay together as a whole owing to the precise values of these forces.

When we consider the size of the atom and the number of atoms in the universe, it is impossible to fail to notice that there is tremendous equilibri-um and design at work. It is crystal clear that the fundamental forces in the universe have been created in a very special way with great wisdom and po-wer. The only thing those who reject faith resort to is nothing other than cla-iming that all of these came into being as a result of "coincidences". Probabi-listic calculations, however, scientifically put the probability of the equilibri-ums in the universe being formed "coincidentally" at "0". All these are clear evidence of the existence of Allah and the perfection of His creation.

...My Lord encompasses all things in His knowledge so will you not pay heed? (Surat al-An'am: 80)

The Space in the Atom

As mentioned previously, the greater part of an atom consists of space. This makes everyone think of the same question: why is there such space? Let us think. In simple terms, the atom consists of a nucleus, around which electrons revolve. There is nothing else between the nucleus and the elect-rons. This microscopic distance "in which nothing exists" is in fact a very lar-ge one on the atomic scale. We can exemplify this scale as follows: if a small marble of one centimetre in diameter represents the electron closest to the nucleus, the nucleus would be one kilometre away from this marble.[17] We can cite the following example to make this magnitude clearer in our mind:

There is a great space lying between the basic particles. If I think of the proton of an oxygen nucleus as the head of a pin lying on the table in front of me, then the electron revolving around it draws a circle pas-sing through Holland, Germany and Spain (The writer of these lines lives in France). Therefore, if all atoms forming my body came toget-her so close as to touch each other, you would not be able to see me any more. You would actually never be able to see me with the naked

The space between the protons and electrons of the atom is as wide as the area marked on the above map.

eye. I would be as small as a tiny dust particle of the size of a several thousandth of a millimetre.[18]

At this point, we realise that there is a similarity between the largest and the smallest spaces known in the universe. When we turn our eyes to the stars, there again we see a void similar to that in the atoms. There are voids of billions of kilometres both between the stars and between the galaxies. Yet, in both of these voids, an order that is beyond the understanding of human mind prevails.

Inside the Nucleus: Protons and Neutrons

Until 1932, it was thought that the nucleus only consisted of protons and electrons. It was discovered then that there are not electrons but neutrons in the nucleus besides the protons. (The renowned scientist Chadwick proved in 1932 the existence of neutrons in the nucleus and he was awarded a Noble Prize for his discovery). Mankind was introduced to the real structure of the atom only at such a recent date.

We had mentioned before how small is the nucleus of the atom. The size of a proton that is able to fit in the atomic nucleus is 10^{-15} metres.

You may think that such a small particle would not have any meaning in one's life. However, these particles that are so small as to be incomprehensible by the human mind form the basis of everything you see around you.

Source of the Diversity in the Universe

There are 109 elements that so far have been identified. The entire universe, our earth, and all animate and inanimate beings are formed by the arrangement of these 109 elements in various combinations. Thus far, we saw that all elements are made up of atoms that are similar to each other, which, in turn are made up of the same particles. So, if all the atoms constituting the elements are made up of the same particles, what then is it that makes the elements different from each other and causes the formation of infinitely diverse matters?

It is the number of protons in the nuclei of the atoms that principally differentiates the elements from each other. There is one proton in the hydrogen atom, the lightest element, 2 protons in the helium atom, the second lightest element, 79 protons in the gold atom, 8 protons in the oxygen atom and 26 protons in the iron atom. What differentiates gold from iron and iron from oxygen is simply the different numbers of protons in their atoms. The air we breathe, our bodies, the plants and animals, planets in space, animate and inanimate, bitter and sweet, solid and liquid, everything… all of these are ultimately made up of protons, neutrons and electrons.

The Borderline of Physical Existence: the Quarks

Until 20 years ago, it was believed that the smallest particles making up the atoms were protons and neutrons. Yet, most recently, it has been discovered that there are much smaller particles in the atom that form the above-mentioned particles.

This discovery led to the development of a branch of physics called

What causes the difference between the elements is the number of protons in the nuclei of their atoms. It is this difference that makes the materials shown above appear so different from each other.

"Particle Physics" investigating the "sub-particles" within the atom and their particular movements. Research conducted by particle physics revealed that the protons and neutrons making up the atom are actually formed of sub-particles called "quarks".

The dimension of the quarks that form the proton, which is so small as to exceed the capabilities of human imagination, is much more astounding: 10^{-18} (0.000000000000000001) metres.

The quarks inside a proton can never be pulled apart from each other very much because the "strong nuclear force" that is responsible for keeping the particles inside the nucleus together operates here as well. This force serves as a rubber band between the quarks. As the distance between the quarks increases, so does this force and two quarks cannot become more distant from each other than a quadrillionth of a metre. These rubber bands bet-

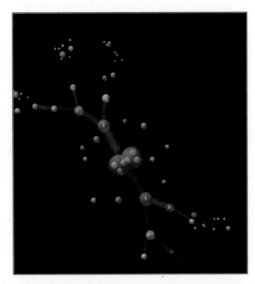

The protons and neutrons in the nucleus of the atom are formed from smaller particles called quarks.

ween the quarks are formed by gluons that possess the strong nuclear force. The quarks and the gluons have a very strong interaction. However, scientists have not yet been able to discover how this interaction takes place.

Research is underway in the field of "Particle Physics" to unravel the world of sub-atomic particles. Yet, despite all the intellect, consciousness and knowledge mankind possesses, we have only recently been able to discover the very basic particles forming everything, including ourselves. Further, the more we delve into these particles, the more detailed the subject becomes, leaving us in the lurch at the limit of the 10^{-18} m dimension of the quark. So, what lies beyond this limit?

Today, scientists propound various hypotheses on this subject, but as mentioned above, this limit is the furthest point hitherto reached in the material universe. Everything beyond that point can only be expressed as energy, not as matter. The really important point is that man finds, in a location that he has only just been able to discover with all the technological means at his disposal, enormous balances and the laws of physics already running like a clock. Furthermore, this location is inside the atom, which constitutes the building block of all matter in the universe, as well as of human beings.

Man has just started to become aware of the perfect mechanism functioning without fail in the organs and systems in his own body. His discovery of the mechanisms of the cells forming these structures goes back only a few decades. The supreme creation evident in the atoms lying at the basis of cells, the protons and neutrons in the atoms, and the quarks in these particle is so perfect as to stagger everyone, be him believer or not. The basic point to be pondered here is that all of these perfect mechanisms run in an orderly fashion every second throughout man's life, without any intervention by him, and totally outside his control. It is very self-evident fact to everyone who uses his conscience and wisdom that all of these have been created by Allah, Owner of superior power and knowledge, and are governed by Him.

Everyone in the heavens and earth requests His aid. Every day He is engaged in some affair. So which of your Lord's blessings do you then deny? (Surat ar-Rahman: 29-30)

The Other Aspect of the Atoms: Electrons

Electrons are particles spinning and revolving around the nucleus of the atom similar to the earth rotating on its own axis as it also revolves around the sun. This rotation, like that of the planets, is realised ceaselessly and in perfect order on paths we call orbits. Yet, the proportion of the size of the earth and

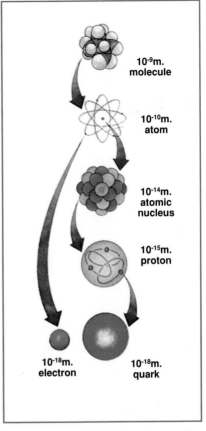

10^{-9}m.
molecule

10^{-10}m.
atom

10^{-14}m.
atomic
nucleus

10^{-15}m.
proton

10^{-18}m.
electron

10^{-18}m.
quark

From the structure of the atom to the structure of the quark, it is possible to analyse the smallest particles forming the atom using modern accelerators. The diagram above illustrates this relationship in a progressive fashion.

the sun is very different from the atomic scale. To make a comparison between the size of electrons and the size of the earth, if we enlarge an atom as big as the earth, the electron would be in the size of an apple.[19]

Tens of electrons revolving in an area so small as to be invisible even to the most powerful microscopes create a very complex traffic inside the atom. The most remarkable point here is that these electrons surrounding the nucleus like an armour of electrical charge do not have even a small accident. In

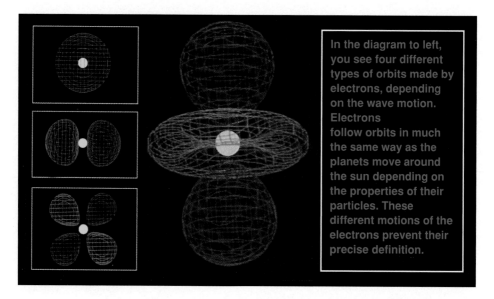

In the diagram to left, you see four different types of orbits made by electrons, depending on the wave motion. Electrons follow orbits in much the same way as the planets move around the sun depending on the properties of their particles. These different motions of the electrons prevent their precise definition.

fact, any small accident inside the atom would cause a disaster for the atom. However, such an accident never takes place. The whole operation runs flawlessly. The electrons revolving around the nucleus at the mind-boggling speed of 1,000 km/second never collide with each other. It is extremely amazing that these electrons, which are no different from each other, follow separate orbits, and it is obviously the result of a "conscious creation". If they had different masses and velocities, it might be natural for them to settle in different orbits around the nucleus. For instance, the order of the planets in our solar system follows this logic. Planets that have totally different masses and velocities are naturally settled in different orbits around the sun. But the case with the electrons in the atom is totally different from that of these planets. The electrons are exactly alike but have different orbits around the nucleus: how do they follow these paths unerringly, how do they not collide though they have incredibly small dimensions and move at incredible speeds? These questions lead us to a single point: the only truth we face in this unique order and delicate equilibrium is the perfect creation of Allah.

He is Allah – the Creator, the Maker, the Giver of Form. To Him belong the Most Beautiful Names. Everything in the heavens and earth glorifies Him. He is the Almighty, the All-Wise. (Surat al-Hashr: 24)

Electrons are small particles, almost two thousandth the size of neutrons and protons. An atom has the same number of electrons as protons and each electron bears a negative (-) charge equal to the positive (+) charge borne by each proton. The total positive (+) charge in the nucleus and the total negative (-) charge of the electrons cancel each other and the atom becomes neutral.

The electric charge they carry obliges electrons to obey certain laws of physics. One of these laws of physics is that "same electrical charges repel each other and opposite charges attract each other".

First, under normal circumstances, the electrons, all negatively charged, would be expected to repel each other by obeying this rule and shoot away from the nucleus. Yet, this does not happen. If the electrons were scattered from the nucleus, then the universe would consist of idle protons, neutrons and electrons wandering in the void. Second, the positively charged nucleus would be expected to attract the negative charged electrons and the electrons would stick to the nucleus. In that case, the nucleus would attract all the electrons and the atom would implode.

However, none of these things occur. The abovementioned extraordinary escape velocities of the electrons (1,000 km/sec), the repelling force they exert on each other and the force of attraction the nucleus exerts on the electrons are based on such precise values that these three contradicting factors perfectly balance each other. As a result, this outstanding system inside the atom runs without falling apart. Even if a single one of these forces impinging on the atom were a little bit more or less than it has to be, the atom would never exist.

In addition to these factors, if the nuclear forces binding protons and neutrons in the nucleus to each other did not exist, protons having equal charges could not even come close to each other, much less bond together in a nucleus. In the same manner, the neutrons would never be able to stick to the nucleus. As a result, there would be no nucleus and therefore, no atom.

All these fine calculations are indications that even a single atom is not idle but acts under the perfect control of Allah. Otherwise, it would be inevitable that the universe we live in would end before it started. This process would backfire at the outset and the universe would not form. However, Allah, the Creator of everything, the Omnipotent and the Almighty, established extremely precise equilibriums inside the atom just as He established all the balances in the universe, thanks to which the atom continues to exist in perfect order.

Scientists have spent their best efforts over the years to unravel the secret of this balance established by Allah, and have ended up with merely appointing certain names to observed phenomena such as "the electromagnetic force", "the strong nuclear force", "the weak nuclear force", and "the mass attraction force"... Yet, as mentioned in the introductory part of the book, no one has given a thought to the question "Why?" Why do these forces act at certain intensities under certain rules? Why do the domains that are governed by these forces, the rules they obey, and the intensity of these forces have such great harmony?

Scientists were desperate in the face of all these questions because all they can do is guess at the order in which the events take place. Their research, however, gave rise to an indisputable reality. Every point in the univer-

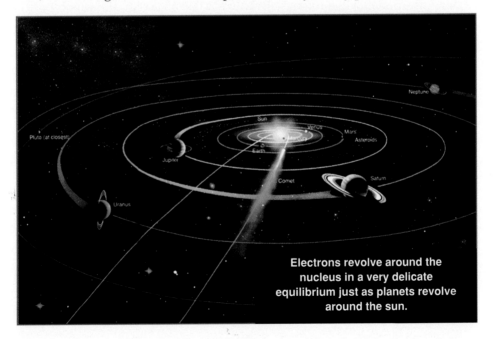

Electrons revolve around the nucleus in a very delicate equilibrium just as planets revolve around the sun.

se reveals the intervention of an Owner of intellect and will Who does not leave even a single atom idle. There is a single power that holds all forces together in harmony, and that is Allah, Who holds all the power and might. Allah manifests His might wherever He wills whenever He wills. The entire

> **In the alternation of night and day and what Allah has created in the heavens and the earth there are Signs for people who fear Him.
> (Surah Yunus: 6)**

universe from the smallest atom to the endless galaxies is able to continue its existence only by Allah's will and preservation.

In the Qur'an, Allah states that there is no power but Him and He announces the punishment of those who, unaware of this, assume that the powerless beings (animate or inanimate) He created have power and strength independently of Him, and attribute divine characteristics to them.

Oh, that those who do evil had but known, (on the day) when they see the punishment, that power belongs wholly to Allah, and that Allah is severe in punishment! (Surat al-Baqara: 165)

So far no scientist has yet been able to explain the cause and source of the forces in the atom and therefore in the universe, and why certain forces come into play on certain occasions. What science does is only to make observations, take measurements and designate "names" for them.

Such "namings" are regarded as great discoveries in the world of science. In fact, what scientists do is not an attempt to form a new equilibrium in the universe or build a new system but just an effort to comprehend and unravel the secret of the evident equilibrium in the cosmos. What they mostly do is simply observe one of the countless wonders of Allah's creation in the universe and assigning a name to it. Scientists detecting a superior system or structure created by Allah are awarded various scientific prizes, honoured and admired by other people. In this case, the one who really should be honoured is, without doubt, Allah, the Most Gracious, the Most Merciful, Who brought that system into being when it was not, furnished it with exceedingly delicate balances, and endlessly creates extraordinary miracles the like of them.

Studying the particles that are the building blocks of matter is possible by investigating particles that are millions of times smaller than the atom. Research on these extremely minute particles may only be carried out using very enormous and complex particle physics experimental apparatuses. Such highly complex experiments can only be controlled with extensive use of computers.

High-energy particle physics is a field of science that studies the building blocks of matter and the interactions between them. Recent experiments carried out by the help of new high technology allow us to rapidly expand our knowledge on the composition of matter. Research on particle physics is conducted in particle accelerator laboratories kilometres in diameter. In particle accelerators, charged particles – mostly protons and electrons – are accelerated to great velocities in an electromagnetic field and directed into a cloud chamber. The accelerated particles are then made to collide with either fixed targets or with each other. The particles shattered as a result of these collisions are examined by various detector systems.

The accelerator and detector technologies, whose sophistication increasingly progressed from the 1950's on, made very high-energy collisions possible. The study of these collisions by advanced detector systems gave way to the discovery that protons and neutrons, known as the basis of matter, have a sub-structure composed of particles called quarks. Measurements made at high energy levels gave scientists the opportunity to study the composition of matter at distances as small as one hundredth of the radius of the proton. Accelerator laboratories are found only in a few centres in the world as their foundation and operation are very costly. The most important ones are CERN (Geneva), DESY (Hamburg), Fermilab-FNAL (Chicago) and SLC (California). High-energy physicists participate in experimental studies in these centres in large groups and study the secrets of the atom. Among these laboratories, the SLC is 3 km in diameter and CERN 27 km. However, the champion in the competition for size is the US project SSC which is being constructed in the centre of Texas in the USA, with a perimeter diameter of about 85 kilometres. The cost of the machinery increases in direct proportion to size (For SSC, this figure will be approximately 6 billion dollars).[20]

The CERN particle physics laboratory uses a tube 100 metres underground running in a 27 kilometres diameter circle. Particles are first accelerated in this long tube, and then made to collide with each other.

The CERN particle physics laboratory is an international research centre located on the Swiss–French border and formed by a membership of 19 European nations. The research subject of this laboratory is the basic structure of matter and the main particles forming this structure. About 3,000 physicists, engineers, technicians and administrative personnel are employed in the laboratory, which is visited by over 6,000 member physicists for research purposes.

In the alternation of night and day and what Allah has created in the heavens and the earth there are Signs for people who fear Him. (Surah Yunus: 6)

Orbits of Electrons

Tens of electrons, which spin and orbit in an area unobservable even by the most powerful microscopes, create an extremely complex traffic inside the atom as we mentioned earlier. This traffic, however, is so orderly as to be incomparably more orderly than the most systematic city traffic. Electrons never collide with each other, because each electron has a separate orbit and these orbits never coincide.

There are 7 electron shells around the nucleus of the atom. The numbers of electrons in these seven electron shells that never change have been specified by a mathematical formula: $2n^2$. The maximum numbers of electrons that can be present in each electron shell around the atom have been fixed by

ELECTRONS IN THE SERVICE OF MANKIND

Electricity is one of the most important parts of our life. We apparently cannot do anything without it. Our lives are tied to electricity when we eat, watch TV, go from one place to another or do cleaning. We push a button and everything around us is lit up. We push another button and all electrical devices start working. This form of electricity we use each moment of our lives is called the electric current. What make this current possible are the electrons we have been reviewing since the beginning of this book. Electricity is the charged current formed as a result of the movement of negative (-) charged electrons and ions. Devices like television and the refrigerator in ordinary use draw 1-2 ampere electricity. So, what does this amount mean?

A current of 1 ampere per second means the transmission of 6 billion times a billion electrons from a given section per second. This figure is one million times more for a bolt of lightning.

this formula. (The letter n in the formula shows the electron shell number).

That the endless number of electron shells of atoms making up the universe precisely stick to the same number by obeying the $2n^2$ formula indicates order. That no chaos occurs inside the atom although the electrons move about at incredible speeds is a further indication of this unique order. This is an order that can by no means be attributed to coincidence. The only explanation for the existence of this order is that Allah created everything as a manifestation of His power in an order and harmony as told in the Qur'an. Allah refers to this order He created in the verses of the Qur'an:

...Allah has appointed a measure for all things. (Surat at-Talaq: 3)

...He created everything and determined it most exactly. (Surat al-Furqan: 2)

Everything has its measure with Him, the Knower of the Unseen and the Visible, the Most Great, the High-Exalted. (Surat ar-R'ad: 8-9)

As for the earth, We stretched it out and cast firmly embedded mountains in it and made everything grow in due proportion on it. (Surat al-Hijr: 19)

The sun and the moon both run with precision. (Surat ar-Rahman: 5)

He erected heaven and established the balance. (Surat ar-Rahman: 7)

Electrons follow an extremely complex orbit within the atom. Although a much more crowded environment than city traffic is formed in such a small place, not even one accident takes place.

As the verses reveal, Allah, the Lord of all the worlds, is He Who creates everything in perfect proportion, measure and order. This proportion and measure cover the entire realm of beings from the smallest sub-atomic particle to the gigantic celestial bodies in space: solar systems, galaxies and everything between them. This is the outcome of the endless and infinite might, knowledge, artistry and wisdom of Allah. Allah introduces His attributes to human beings in the perfect measure, order, and equilibrium in the beings and systems He creates. He displays His endless power before our very eyes. This is the truth to which all scientific research and calculations must lead man.

Wave or Particle?

When electrons were first discovered, they were thought to be particles like the protons and neutrons found in the nucleus. In the experiments that followed, however, it was discovered that they display wave characteristics like light particles, that is, photons. Subsequently, quantum physicists came to the conclusion that every particle is simultaneously a wave form with its own distinct frequency.

SIGNS FROM THE QUR'AN

When studying the subject of electron shells, one must also think over a verse pointing to this subject in the Qur'an. There are 7 electron shells around the nucleus of the atom. On each shell are electrons in fixed numbers. Could it be that the expression "the seven heavens" used in the Qur'an to describe the layers forming the heavens, may also be pointing to the orbits electron shells that are as if the heavens of the atom?

He Who created the seven heavens in layers. You will not find any flaw in the creation of the All-Merciful. Look again – do you see any gaps? (Surat al-Mulk: 3)

This figure never changes. It never becomes 6 or 8. Here, the really miraculous thing is that this figure of seven electron shells is in total harmony with the verse.

It is known that light is spread in a way similar to the ripples created on the surface of water when a stone is throne into a lake. However, light sometimes bears the characteristic of a particle of matter and is observed in the form of sporadic, intermittent pulses like rain drops falling on a window-pane. This same dichotomy was experienced in the electron as well, which led to great confusion in the world of science. The following words of Richard P. Feynman, the renowned Professor of Theoretical Physics, was to lay the whole confusion to rest:

> Now we know how the electrons and light behave. But what can I call it? If I say they behave like particles I give the wrong impression; also if I say they behave like waves. They behave in their own inimitable way, which technically could be called a quantum mechanical way. They behave in a way that is like nothing that you have ever seen before... An atom does not behave like a weight hanging on a spring and oscillating. Nor does it behave like a miniature representation of the solar system with little planets going around in orbits. Nor does it appear to be so-

mewhat like a cloud or fog of some sort surrounding the nucleus. It behaves like nothing you have ever seen before. There is one simplification at least. Electrons behave in this respect in exactly the same way as photons; they are both screwy, but in exactly the same way. How they behave, therefore, takes a great deal of imagination to appreciate, because we are going to describe something that is different from anything you know about. [21]

Because scientists were never able to explain the behaviour of electrons, as a solution they gave a new name to it: "Quantum Mechanical Motion". Let us again quote from Professor Feynman who in the following words states the exceptional nature of that and the awe he feels:

> Do not keep saying to yourself, if you can possibly avoid it, 'But how can it be like that?' because you will get 'down the drain', into a blind alley from which nobody has yet escaped. Nobody knows how it can be like that. [22]

Yet, the blind alley Feynman refers to here is actually not so. The reason why some people can never figure a way out of this dilemma is that despite substantial evidence, they cannot accept that these incredible systems and equilibriums have been brought into existence by the sublime Creator. The situation is extremely clear: Allah created the universe when it was not, furnished it with extraordinary balances and brought it into being without any preceding example. The answer to the scientists' question "How can it be like that?" that can never be solved, nor understood, lies in the fact that Allah is the Creator of everything and that everything exists only by His command "Be!"

> **To Him is due the primal origin of the heavens and the earth. When He decides on something, He just says to it, 'Be!' and it is. (Surat al-Baqarah: 117)**

The World Full of Colour Whose Gates are Opened by Electrons

Have you ever thought what it would be like to live in a world without colour? Try to visualise your body, the people around you, the seas, the sky, trees, flowers, in short, everything in black. You would never want to live in such a world, would you?

What makes the earth colourful? How do the colours, which make our world so extraordinarily beautiful, come into being?

Certain characteristics present in the nature of matter allow us perceive objects in colour. Colours are formed as a natural result of certain motions of the electrons inside the atom. You may think "What do the motions of electrons have to do with colours?" Let's briefly explain this relationship:

Electrons revolve only in electron shells. We just mentioned that there are 7 electron shells. Each electron shell has a specific level of energy, which varies depending on the distance of the shell from the nucleus. The closer an electron shell is to the nucleus, the less energy its electrons have, and the farther it is to the nucleus, the more energy its electrons have.

Each electron shell has "sub-shells", among which the electrons of that shell continuously move.

An electron needs to receive external energy to be able to travel outwards between the shells. The source of this energy is the "photon".

In its simplest terms, the photon is a "light particle". Every star in the universe is a source of photons. The most important source of photons for

our world is, of course, the sun. Photons are diffused throughout space from the sun at a speed of 300,000 km a second.

When these photons, arriving on earth from the sun, strike the atoms of objects on earth, the electrons of atoms sometimes begin their travel. If the electrons that are able to travel by the help of this energy rise to a higher energy shell and then return to their own shell, they emit a photon that is to form the colour that will meet our eye. Each one of these processes summarized in the few sentences above has been continuing since the outset of creation without fail. Every step runs under a great plan and to order. If only one part of this interaction between electrons and photons had not worked, this would cause a colourless, dark universe.

Let us again list these steps that have to work according to plan and in order for the formation of a universe with colours instead of a dark one.

♦ Light coming from the sun to the earth diffuses in the form of photon particles. These photon particles scattered around the earth strike atoms of matters.

♦ Photons cannot travel a long way inside the atoms. They strike the electrons circling the nucleus.

♦ Electrons absorb these photons that strike them.

♦ When the electrons take in the energy of the photons they absorb, they jump to another shell having a higher level of energy.

♦ These electrons try to return to their original states.

♦ As they return to their own shells, they emit an energy charged photon.

♦ These photons emitted by the electrons determine the colour of that object.

To sum up, the colour of an object in fact consists of a mixture of these light particles that are absorbed, then emitted by this object, and reach our eyes. The colour of an object that does not emit light itself but reflects the light it receives from the sun depends both on the light it receives and the change it makes on this light. If the object illuminated with white light appears "red", this is because it absorbs a large portion of the mixture that arrives to it from the sunrays and emits only red. By saying "it absorbs", we mean

70% of the rays reaching our earth from the sun are just appropriate for the existence of life on the earth.

the following:

As mentioned before, every shell has sub-shells and electrons travel between these sub-shells. Each shell corresponds to a specific level of energy, and electrons carry as much energy as allowed by the energy level of the shell on which they circle. Shells that are more distant from the nucleus, have higher energy. When a space for one electron becomes available in an upper shell, the electron suddenly disappears, and then re-appears again in that sub-shell with higher energy level. Yet, in order for the electron to perform this, it has to raise its energy level to the level required by the shell to which it jumps. The electron increases its energy level by absorbing (swallowing) photon particles coming from the sun.

We can make the situation clearer with a few examples. Let us consider the Morpho Butterfly. The pigments on the butterfly absorb the entire sunlight re-emitting only the colour blue. When the light particles for that reflec-

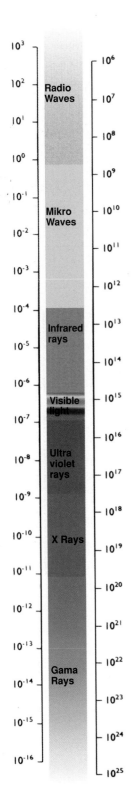

ted colour reach the retina in the eye, they are converted to electrical signals by the cone cells in the retina in such a way to be perceived as blue and sent to the brain. Eventually, the colour blue is formed in the brain.

This means that the colour of an object depends on the character of the light emitted from the light source and how much of this light is re-emitted by the object in question. For instance, the colour of a dress is not the same under sunlight and in a store. If an object is perceived as black by our brain, it means that this object absorbs all the light coming from the sun reflecting none to the outside. In the same manner, if the object reflects all light coming from the sun and does not absorb any of it, then it is perceived as white by our brain. In this case, the points that need careful consideration are the following:

1. The colour of an object depends on the properties of the light emitted by the light source.

2. The colour of an object depends on the reaction of the electrons of the molecules in its structure, as to which light these electrons will absorb and which they will not.

3. The colour of an object depends on how our brain will perceive the photon striking the retina.

Here, let us stop and think once more.

The electrons that revolve at incredible speed around the nucleus of the atom, which is a matter too small to be seen with the eye, suddenly disappear from their own shells and jump to another place called a sub-shell. There also needs to be a space available on the sub-shell for this leap. They are supplied the energy they require

A great variety of rays arrive on the earth from the sun. As seen in the electromagnetic spectrum to left, we only perceive a very small portion of these rays.

The superior design in the formation of colours leads us to a single fact: the universe has been created in a great harmony and order from its smallest to its largest particles. The artistry in the colours is one of the signs of Allah's perfect creation.

during the process by absorbing photons. They then go back to their original orbits. During this action, colours perceivable by the human eye are formed. What's more, atoms in number expressible in trillions keep doing this every moment, thanks to which we are able to view an uninterrupted "image".

This magnificent mechanism is not comparable to the operation of any man-made machine. A clock, for instance, has a highly complex mechanism in itself, and all the parts of a clock (gears, discs, screws, nuts, etc.) must be located in the right places in the right way for a clock to work properly. The smallest problem in this mechanism would impede the mechanism of the clock. Yet, when we think of the structure of an atom and how the above-mentioned mechanism of the electrons works, the simplicity of the structure of a clock is better understood. As we said, the mechanism of the electrons is too complex, perfect and flawless to be compared to any man-made system. Definitely, a system that has such mind-boggling complexity and runs so perfectly could not have come about spontaneously, as a result of coincidence, as claimed by materialist scientists. Let us now ask the following question: if you saw a working clock on the ground while walking in a desert, would you think that this had formed out of dust, sand, soil and stones by chance? Nobody would think that, because the design and wisdom in the clock are all too obvious. However the design and wisdom in a single atom are, as we mentioned above, incomparably superior to those in any man-made mechanism. The owner of this wisdom is Allah, Who has supreme knowled-

Photons coming from the sun make it possible for us to see a world full of colour by impinging on the structure of the objects on the earth.

ge, Who knows, sees and creates everything.

Allah created every 'where' both that which we are able to see and that which we cannot, with boundless artistry and He gave innumerable favours to be at our service, whether we are aware of them or not. The subject of colours about which we previously knew nothing, and felt no need to learn, has been brought to our attention in all its details and complexity as science advanced. It is undeniable that scientific development and progress ought to cause everyone who uses his wisdom and conscience to believe in the existence of Allah. Nonetheless, people still exist who ignore the superior artistry and wisdom observable at every point in the universe. The acclaimed scientist, Louis Pasteur made an interesting remark on this subject saying "Little science takes you away from God but more of it takes you to Him".[23]

As a person learns more about the examples of creation surrounding him, he grasps much better that Allah encompasses him from every direction,

He directs all affairs in heaven and earth, and holds everything under control. He understands that his life will certainly be taken and he will be answerable for everything he has done on earth. As a believer becomes more acquainted with the innumerable phenomena taking place around him, his admiration for Allah's knowledge increasingly grows. This admiration is a very important step on the way to perceiving the infinite power and might of Allah as much as possible and fearing Him as required. This is stated in the Qur'an:

Do you not see that Allah sends down water from the sky and by it We bring forth fruits of varying colours? And in the mountains there are streaks of white and red, of varying shades, and rocks of deep jet black. And mankind and beasts and livestock are likewise of varying colours. Only those of His slaves with knowledge have fear of Allah. Allah is Almighty, Ever-Forgiving. (Surah Fatir: 27-28)

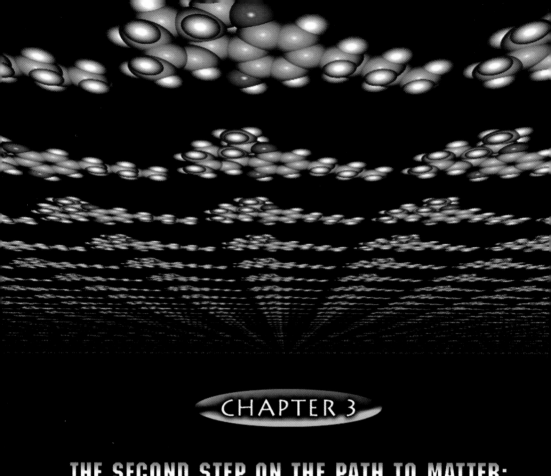

CHAPTER 3

THE SECOND STEP ON THE PATH TO MATTER: MOLECULES

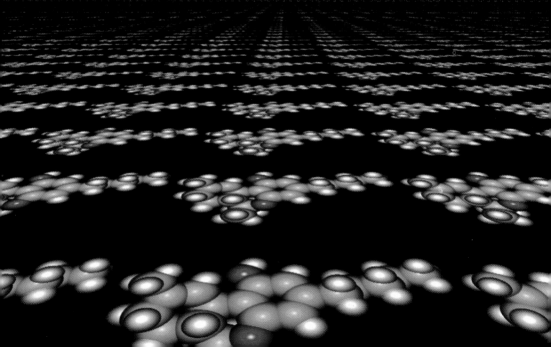

What is it that makes the objects you see in your surroundings different from each other? What is it that discriminates their colours, shapes, smells, and tastes? Why is one substance soft, another hard, and yet another fluid? From what you have read so far, you may answer these questions saying, "The differences between their atoms do this". Yet, this answer is not sufficient, because if the atoms were the cause for these differences, then there would have to be billions of atoms bearing different properties from each other. In practice, this is not so. Many materials look different and bear different properties although they contain the same atoms. The reason for this is the different chemical bonds the atoms form among them to become molecules.

On the way to matter, molecules are the second step after atoms. Molecules are the smallest units determining the chemical properties of matter. These small bodies are made up of two or more atoms and some, of thousands of groups of atoms. Atoms are held together inside molecules by chemical bonds determined by the electromagnetic force of attraction, which means that these bonds are formed on the basis of the electrical charges of the atoms. The electrical charges of atoms, in turn, are determined by the electrons on their outermost shell. The arrangement of molecules in different combinations give rise to the diversity of matter we see around us. The importance of the chemical bonds that lie at the heart of the diversity of matter come forward at this very point.

Chemical Bonds

As explained above, chemical bonds are formed through the motion of electrons in the outermost electron shells of the atoms. Each atom has a tendency to fill up its outermost shell with the maximum number of electrons it may shelter. The maximum number of electrons the atoms can hold in their outermost shells is 8. To do this, atoms either receive electrons from other atoms to complete the electrons in their outermost shells to eight, or if they have lesser electrons in their outermost shells, then they give these to another atom, making a sub-shell that had previously been completed in their outermost orbits. The tendency of the atoms to exchange electrons constitutes the basic inciting force of the chemical bonds they form between each other.

67

This driving force, that is, the objective of the atoms to raise the number of electrons in their outermost shells to maximum, causes an atom to form three types of bonds with other atoms. These are the ionic bond, covalent bond and metallic bond.

Commonly, special bonds categorised under the general title of "weak bonds" act between molecules. These bonds are weaker than the bonds formed by atoms to constitute molecules because molecules need more flexible structures to form matter.

Let us now, in brief, see the properties of these bonds and how they are formed.

Ionic Bonds

Atoms combined by this bond swap electrons to complete the number of electrons in their outermost shells to eight. Atoms having up to four electrons in their outermost shells give these electrons to the atom with which they are going to combine, that is, with which they will bond. Atoms having more than four electrons in their outermost shells receive electrons from the atoms with which they will bond. Molecules formed by this type of bond have crystal (cubic) structures. Familiar table salt (NaCl) molecules are among substances formed by this bond. Why do atoms have such a tendency? What would happen if they did not have it?

Until today, the bonds formed by atoms could be defined only in very general terms. It has not yet been understood why atoms adhere to this principle. Could it be that atoms decide by themselves that the number of electrons in their outermost shells should be eight? Definitely not. This is such decisive behaviour that it goes beyond the atom, because it has no intellect, will, or consciousness. This number is the key in the combination of atoms as molecules that constitute the first step in the creation of the matter, and even-

The sodium atom gives its outermost electron to a chlorine atom and becomes positively charged. Receiving the electron, the chlorine atom becomes negatively charged. The two form an ionic bond through these two opposite charges attracting each other.[24]

Sodium chloride molecule (NaCl)

Sodium atom   Chlorine atom   Sodium ion   Chlorine ion

tually, the universe. If atoms did not have such a tendency based on this principle, molecules, and in turn, matter would not exist. Yet, from the first moment they were created, atoms have been serving in the formation of molecules and matter in a perfect manner thanks to this tendency.

Covalent Bonds

Scientists who studied the bonds between atoms faced an interesting situation. While some atoms swap electrons for bonding, some of them share the electrons in their outermost shells. Further research revealed that many molecules that are of critical importance for life owe their existence to these 'covalent' bonds.

Fluorine atom   Fluorine molecule (F_2)

Water molecule (H_2O)

Hydrogen   Oxygen
atom   atom

Some atoms form new molecules by covalent bonding, sharing the electrons in their outer orbits.[25]

Let us give a simple example to explain covalent bonds better. As we mentioned previously on the subject of electron shells, atoms can carry a maximum of two electrons in their innermost electron shells. The hydrogen atom has a single electron and it has the tendency to increase the number of its electrons to two to become a stable atom. Therefore, the hydrogen atom forms a covalent bond with a second hydrogen atom. That is, the two hydrogen atoms share each other's single electron as a second electron. Thus, the H_2 molecule is formed.

Metallic Bonds

If a large number of atoms come together by sharing each others' elect-

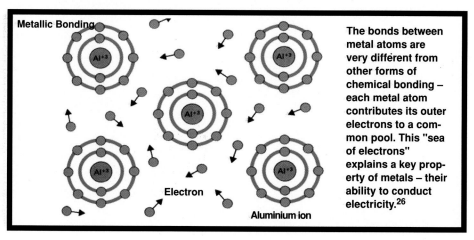

Metallic Bonding

Electron

Aluminium ion

The bonds between metal atoms are very different from other forms of chemical bonding – each metal atom contributes its outer electrons to a common pool. This "sea of electrons" explains a key property of metals – their ability to conduct electricity.[26]

rons, this is called a "metallic bond". Metals like iron, copper, zinc, aluminium, etc., that form the raw material of many tools and instruments we see around us or use in daily life, have acquired a substantial and tangible body as a result of the metallic bonds formed by the atoms constituting them.

Scientists are not able to answer the question as to why electrons in the electron shells of the atoms have such a tendency. Living organisms, most interestingly, owe their existence to this tendency.

The Next Step: Compounds

Do you wonder how many different compounds these bonds can form?

In laboratories, new compounds are produced everyday. Currently, it is possible to talk about almost two million compounds. The simplest chemical compound can be as small as the hydrogen molecule, while there are also compounds made up of millions of atoms.[27]

How many different compounds can an element form at most? The answer to this question is quite interesting because, on the one hand, there are certain elements that do not interact with any others (inert gases), while, on the other hand, there is the carbon atom that is able to form 1,700,000 compounds. As stated above, the total number of compounds is about two million. 108 elements out of the total of 109 form 300,000 compounds. Carbon, however, forms 1,700,000 compounds all by itself in a most amazing fashion.

The Raw Materials of the Universe and the Periodic Table: 92 elements found freely in nature and 17 elements formed artificially in laboratories or in nuclear reactions are arranged in a table called the "Periodic Table" according to the number of their protons. At first look, the Periodic Table may appear to be a bunch of boxes containing one or two letters with numbers at the top and bottom corners. Most interestingly, however, this table accommodates the elements of the entire universe including the air we breathe, as well as of our bodies.

The Building Block of Life: the "Carbon" Atom

Carbon is the most vital element for living beings, because all living organisms are constructed from compounds of carbon. Numerous pages would not be enough to describe the properties of the carbon atom, which is extremely important for our existence. Nor has the science of chemistry yet been able to discover all of its properties. Here we will mention only a few of the very important properties of carbon.

Carbon atom

Structures as diverse as the cell membrane, the horns of an elk, the trunk of a redwood, the lens of the eye, and the venom of a spider are composed of carbon compounds. Carbon, combined with hydrogen, oxygen, and nitrogen in many different quantities and geometric arrangements, results in a vast assortment of materials with vastly different properties. So, what is the reason for carbon's ability to form approximately 1.7 million compounds?

O 49.5%

Si 25.8%

Al 7.6%

One of the most significant properties of carbon is its ability to form chains very easily by lining carbon atoms up one after another. The shortest carbon chain is made up of two carbon atoms. Despite the unavailability of an exact figure on the number of carbons that make up the longest carbon chain, we can talk about a chain with seventy links. If we consider that the atom that can form the longest chain after the carbon atom is the silicon atom forming six links, the exceptional position of the carbon atom will be better understood.[28]

The reason for carbon's ability to form chains with so many

links is because its chains are not exclusively linear. Chains may be branched, as they may also form polygons.

At this point, the form of the chain plays a very important role. In two carbon compounds, for example, if the carbon atoms are the same in number yet combined in different forms of chains, two different substances are formed. The abovementioned characteristics of the carbon atom produce molecules that are critical for life.

Some carbon compounds' molecules consist of just a few atoms; others contain thousands or even millions. Also, no other element is as versatile as carbon in forming molecules with such durability and stability. To quote David Burnie in his book *Life*:

THREE SIMILAR MOLECULES
RESULT: THREE VERY DIFFERENT SUBSTANCES

Even a difference in a few atoms between molecules leads to very different results. For instance, look carefully at the two molecules written below. They both seem very similar except for very small differences in their carbon and hydrogen components. The result is two totally opposite substances:

$$C_{18}H_{24}O_2 \text{ and } C_{19}H_{28}O_2$$

Can you guess what these molecules are? Let us tell you immediately: the first is oestrogen, the other is testosterone. That is, the former is the hormone responsible for female characteristics and the latter is the hormone responsible for male characteristics. Most interestingly, even a difference of a few atoms can cause sexual differences.

Now take a look at the formula below.

$$C_6H_{12}O_2$$

Doesn't this molecule look very much alike the oestrogen and testosterone hormone molecules? So, what is this molecule, is it another hormone? Let us answer right away: this is the sugar molecule.

From the examples of these three molecules made up of elements of the same type, it is very clear how diverse the substances are that the difference in the number of atoms may produce. On the one hand, there are the hormones responsible for sexual characteristics, while on the other hand, there is sugar, a basic food.

Carbon is a very unusual element. Without the presence of carbon and its unusual properties, it is unlikely that there would be life on Earth.[29]

Diamond, which is a very valuable stone, is a derivative of carbon, which is otherwise commonly found in nature as graphite.

Concerning the importance of carbon for living beings, the British chemist Nevil Sidgwick writes in *Chemical Elements and Their Compounds:*

> Carbon is unique among the elements in the number and variety of the compounds which it can form. Over a quarter of a million have already been isolated and described, but this gives a very imperfect idea of its powers, since it is the basis of all forms of living matter.[30]

The class of compounds formed exclusively from carbon and hydrogen are called "hydrocarbons". This is a huge family of compounds that include natural gas, liquid petroleum, kerosene, and lubricating oils. The hydrocarbons ethylene and propylene form the basis of the petrochemical industry. Hydrocarbons like benzene, toluene, and turpentine are familiar to anyone who's worked with paints. The naphthalene that protects our clothes from moths is another hydrocarbon. Hydrocarbons combined with chlorine or fluorine form anaesthetics, the chemicals used in fire extinguishers and the Freons used in refrigeration.

As the chemist Sidgwick stated above, the human mind is insufficient to fully understand the potential of this atom that has only six protons, six neutrons and six electrons. It is impossible for even a single property of this atom, which is vital for life, to form by chance. The carbon atom, like everything else, has been created by Allah perfectly adapted for the bodies of living beings, which Allah encompasses down to their very atoms.

What is in the heavens and in the earth belongs to Allah. Allah encompasses all things. (Surat an-Nisa': 126)

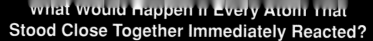

What Would Happen If Every Atom That Stood Close Together Immediately Reacted?

We just said that the whole universe is formed by the interaction of the atoms of 109 different elements. Here, there is a point that needs to be mentioned, which is that a very important condition must be fulfilled for the reaction to start. For instance, water does not form whenever oxygen and hydrogen come together and iron does not rust away as soon as it comes in contact with air. If it did so, iron, which is a hard and shiny metal, would be transformed into ferrous oxide, which is a soft powder, in a few minutes. No such thing as a metal would be left on earth and the order of the world would be greatly disturbed. If atoms that happened to be placed close to each other at a certain distance had united immediately without the fulfilment of certain conditions, atoms of two different substances would have interacted right away. In that case, it would be impossible even for you to sit on a chair, because the atoms forming the chair would immediate react with the atoms forming your body and you would become a being between chair and human (!). Of course, in such a world, life would be out of the question. How is such an end avoided?

To give an example, hydrogen and oxygen molecules react very slowly at room temperature. That means that water forms very slowly at room temperature. Yet, as the temperature of the environment rises, the energies of molecules also increase and reaction is accelerated, and thus water is formed more rapidly.

The minimum amount of energy required for molecules to react with each other is called the "activation energy". For instance, in order for hydrogen and oxygen molecules to react with each other to form water, their energy has to be higher than the activation energy.

Just consider. If the temperature on earth were a little higher, the atoms would react too rapidly, which would destroy the equilibrium in nature. If the opposite were true, that is the temperature on earth were lower, then atoms would react too slowly, which would again disturb the equilibrium in nature. As this clarifies, the distance of the earth from the sun is just appropriate to support life on earth. Certainly, the delicate balances required for life do not end there. The inclination in the axis of the earth, its mass, surface area, the proportion of the gases in its atmosphere, the distance between the earth and its satellite, the moon, and many other factors have to be precisely at their present values so that living beings can survive. This points to the fact that all these factors could not have formed progressively by chance and that they were all created by Allah, the Owner of Supreme power, Who knows all the properties of living beings.

Typically, the role of science during these processes is just to name the laws of physics that it observes. As we explained in the beginning, in the case of such phenomena, questions like "what?", "how?", and "in what way?" fade into insignificance. What we can reach by these questions are only the details of an already existing law. The main questions that should be asked are "why?" and "by whom was this law created"? The answer to these questions remains an enigma for scientists who blindly adhere to their materialist dogmas.

At this point, where materialists reach a deadlock, the picture is very clear for a person who looks at events by using his mind and conscience. The flawless balances in the universe, which cannot be explained as coincidences, have been brought about at the bidding of a supreme mind and will, as stated in the verse, "Allah takes account of everything." (Surat an-Nisa: 86), and He created everything according to a very precise calculation, order and equilibrium.

Intermolecular Bonds: Weak Bonds

The bonds combining the atoms in molecules are much stronger than these weak intermolecular bonds. These bonds can help the formation of millions, and even billions of kinds of molecules.

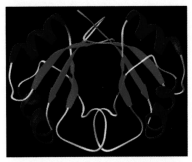

Proteins have to have a special three-dimensional configuration to perform their critical roles in our bodies. Weak bonds between molecules form these structures.

Well, how do molecules combine to form matter?

Since molecules become stable after their formation, they no longer swap atoms.

So, what holds them together?

In an effort to answer this question, chemists produced different theories. Research showed that molecules are able to combine in different ways depending on the properties of the atoms in their composition.

These bonds are very important for organic chemistry, which is the chemistry of living beings, because the most important molecules constituting life are formed due to their ability to form these bonds. Let us take the example of proteins. The complex three-dimensional shapes of proteins, which are the building blocks of living things, are formed thanks to these bonds. This means that the weak chemical bond between molecules is at least as necessary as the strong chemical bond between atoms for the formation of life. Certainly, the strength of these bonds must be of a certain measure.

We can continue with the protein example. Molecules called amino acids combine to form proteins, which are much larger molecules. The atoms forming amino acids are combined by covalent bonds. Weak bonds combine these amino acids in such a way as to produce three-dimensional patterns. Proteins can function in living organisms only if they have these three dimensional patterns. Therefore, if these bonds did not exist, neither would the proteins, or, therefore, life exist.

The "hydrogen" bond, a type of weak bond, plays a major role in the formation of materials that bear great importance in our lives. For instance, the molecules forming water, which is the basis of life, are combined by hydrogen bonds.

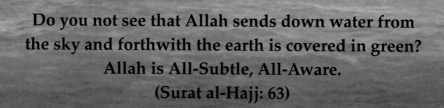

Do you not see that Allah sends down water from
the sky and forthwith the earth is covered in green?
Allah is All-Subtle, All-Aware.
(Surat al-Hajj: 63)

A Miracle Molecule: Water

A liquid specifically chosen for life – "water" – covers two-thirds of our earth. The bodies of all living beings on the earth are formed of this very special liquid at a ratio ranging between 50%-95%. From bacteria living in springs with temperatures close to the boiling point of water, to some special mosses on melting glaciers, life is present everywhere where there is water, no matter at what temperature. Even in a single droplet hung on a leaf after rain, thousands of microscopic living organisms emerge, reproduce, and die.

How would the earth look if there were no water? Certainly, everywhere there would be desert. There would be abysses and horrific pits, in place of seas. The sky would seem cloudless and have a strange colour.

In fact, it is extremely difficult for water, the basis of life on earth, to form. First, let us imagine that hydrogen and oxygen molecules, which are the components of water, are put in a glass bowl. Let us leave them in the bowl for a very long time. These gases may still not form water even if they remain in the bowl for hundreds of years. Even if they do, it would not be more than a very small amount at the very bottom of the bowl and that would happen in a very slow fashion, maybe over thousands of years.

The reason why water forms so slowly under these circumstances is temperature. At room temperature, oxygen and hydrogen react very slowly.

Oxygen and hydrogen, when free, are found as H_2 and O_2 molecules. To combine to form the water molecule, they must collide. As a result of this collision, the bonds forming the hydrogen and oxygen molecules weaken, leaving no hindrance for the combination of oxygen and hydrogen atoms. Temperature raises the energy and therefore, the speed of these molecules, resulting in an increase in the number of collisions. Thus, it accelerates the course of the reaction. However, currently, no temperature high enough to form water exists on earth. The heat required for the formation of water was supplied during the formation of the earth, which resulted in the emergence of so much water as to cover three quarters of the earth's surface. At present, water evaporates and rises to the atmosphere where it cools and returns to the earth in the form of rain. That is, there is no increase in the quantity; only a perpetual cycle.

The Miraculous Properties of Water

Water has many exceptional chemical properties. Every water molecule forms by the combination of hydrogen and oxygen atoms. It is quite interesting that these two gases, one combustive and the other combustible, combine to form a liquid, and most interestingly, water.

Now, let us briefly see how water is formed chemically. The electrical charge of water is zero, that is, it is neutral. Yet, due to the sizes of the oxygen and hydrogen atoms, the oxygen component of the water molecule has a slightly negative charge and its hydrogen component has a slightly positive charge. When more than one water molecule come together, positive and negative charges attract each other to form a very special bond called "the hydrogen bond". The hydrogen bond is a very weak

Water Molecule

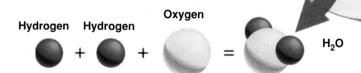

Hydrogen   Hydrogen   Oxygen

$+$ $+$ $=$ H_2O

bond and it is incomprehensibly short-lived. The duration of a hydrogen bond is approximately one hundred billionth of a second. But as soon as a bond breaks, another one forms. Thus, water molecules adhere tightly to each other while also retaining their liquid form because they are combined with a weak bond.

Hydrogen bonds also enable water to resist temperature changes. Even if air temperature increases suddenly, water temperature increases slowly and, similarly, if air temperature falls suddenly, water temperature drops slowly. Large temperature changes are needed to cause considerable changes in water temperature. The significantly high thermal energy of water has major benefits for life. To give a simple example, there is a great amount of water in our bodies. If water adapted to the sudden vicissitudes of temperature in the air at the same rate, we would suddenly develop fevers or freeze.

By the same token, water needs a huge thermal energy to evaporate. Since water uses up a great deal of thermal energy while evaporating, its temperature drops. To give an example, again from the human body, the normal temperature of the body is 36^0 C and the highest body temperature we can tolerate is 42^0 C. This 6^0 C interval is indeed very small and even working under the sun for a few hours can increase body temperature by that amount. Yet, our bodies spend a great amount of thermal energy through sweating, that is, by causing the water it contains to evaporate, which in turn causes body temperature to drop. If our bodies did not have such an automatic mechanism, working for even a few hours under the sun could be fatal.

Hydrogen bonds equip water with yet another extraordinary property, which is water's being more viscous in its liquid state than in its solid state. As a matter of fact, most substances on earth are more viscous in their solid states than in their liquid states. Contrary to other substances, however, water expands as it freezes. This is because hydrogen bonds prevent water molecules from bonding to each other too tightly, and thus many gaps are left in between them. Hydrogen bonds are broken down when water is in liquid state, which causes oxygen atoms to come closer to each other and form a more viscous structure.

This also causes ice to be lighter than water. Normally, if you melt any metal and throw in it a few solid pieces of the same metal, these pieces wo-

If water did not have the property of freezing from the surface downwards, a major portion of the seas would be frozen within a year and life in the sea would be endangered.

Because the density of frozen water is less than water in liquid form, ice floats on water.

uld sink directly to the bottom. In water, however, things are different. Icebergs weighing ten thousands of tons float on water like corks. So, what benefit can this property of water provide us?

Let us answer this question with the example of a river: When the weather is very cold, it is not the whole river, but only the surface of it that freezes. Water reaches its heaviest state at $+ 4^0$ C, and as soon as it reaches this temperature, it immediately sinks to the bottom. Ice is formed on top of water as a layer. Under this layer, water continues to flow, and since $+ 4^0$ C is a temperature at which living organisms can survive, life in water continues.

These unique properties which Allah has given water make life possible on the earth. In the Qur'an, Allah states the importance of this great blessing He offers man:

It is He Who sends down water from the sky. From it you drink and from it come the shrubs among which you graze your herds. And by it He makes crops grow for you and olives and dates and grapes and fruit of every kind. There is certainly a Sign in that for people who reflect. (Surat an-Nahl: 10-11)

An Interesting Property of Water

We all know that water boils at 100^0 C and freezes at 0^0 C. In fact, under normal circumstances, water should be boiling not at 100^0 C but at $+ 180^0$ C. Why?

In the periodic table, the properties of elements in the same group vary in a progressive form from light elements towards heavy elements. This order is most evident in hydrogen compounds. The compounds of the elements sharing the same group with oxygen in the periodic table are called "hydrides". In fact, water is "oxygen hydride". Hydrides of other elements in this group have the same molecular structure as the water molecule.

The boiling points of these compounds vary in a progressive way from sulphur to heavier ones; however, the boiling point of water unexpectedly goes against this pattern. Water (oxygen hydride) boils at 80^0 C less than it is supposed to. Another surprising situation has to do with the freezing point of water. Again, according to the order in the periodic system, water is supposed to freeze at -100^0 C. Yet, water breaks this rule and freezes at 0^0 C, 100^0 C above the temperature at which it is due. This brings to mind the question as to why no other hydride, but only water (oxygen hydride) disobeys the rules of the periodic system.

The laws of physics, the laws of chemistry, and all the other things we name as rules are just attempts at explaining the extraordinary equilibrium in the universe, and the details of creation. All research conducted in the 20th century shows more than ever that all the physical balances in the universe are tailor-made for human life. Research reveals that all the laws of physics, chemistry and biology prevalent in the universe as well as the atmosphere, sun, atoms and molecules, etc., are all arranged just as they are needed in order to support human life. Water, like the other elements mentioned above, is fit for life to such a degree as not to be comparable to any other liquid, and a major portion of the earth is filled with water in just the right amounts required for life. It is obvious that all these cannot be coincidences and that there is perfect order and design prevalent in the universe.

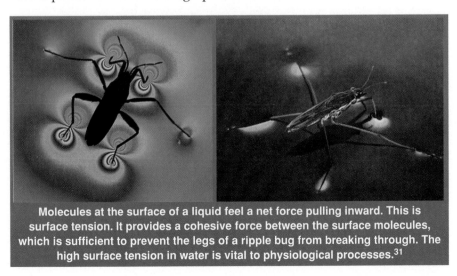

Molecules at the surface of a liquid feel a net force pulling inward. This is surface tension. It provides a cohesive force between the surface molecules, which is sufficient to prevent the legs of a ripple bug from breaking through. The high surface tension in water is vital to physiological processes.[31]

> Allah is He Who created the heavens and the earth and sends down water from the sky and by it brings forth fruits as provision for you. He has made the ships subservient to you to run upon the sea by His command, and He has made the rivers subservient to you, and He has made the sun and moon subservient to you holding steady to their courses, and He has made the night and day subservient to you. He has given you everything you have asked Him for. If you tried to number Allah's blessings, you could never count them. Man is indeed wrongdoing, ungrateful.
> (Surah Ibrahim: 32-34)

The staggering physical and chemical properties of water reveal that this liquid has been created specially for human life. Allah gave life to people through water and by it has brought forth from the earth everything they need in order to live. Allah summons people to think about this subject in the Qur'an:

> It is He Who sends down water from the sky from which We bring forth growth of every kind, and from that We bring forth the green shoots and from them We bring forth close-packed seeds, and from the spathes of the date palm date clusters hanging down, and gardens of grapes and olives and pomegranates, both similar and dissimilar. Look at their fruits as they bear fruit and ripen. There are Signs in that for people who believe. (Surat al-An'am: 99)

The Protective Ceiling: Ozone

The air we breathe, that is, the lower atmosphere, is in the main composed of oxygen gas. By oxygen gas, we mean O_2. That is to say that the oxygen molecules in the lower atmosphere are each comprised of two atoms. However, the oxygen molecule may sometimes be comprised of three atoms (O_3). In this case, this molecule is no longer called oxygen, but "ozone", because these two gases are quite different from each other.

One point needs mention here: while oxygen is formed when two oxygen atoms combine, why is a different gas called ozone formed when three oxygen atoms combine? Eventually, isn't it the oxygen atom that combines, be it two or three atoms in a molecule? Why then do two different gases emerge? Before answering these questions, it would be better to see what differentiates these gasses from each other.

Oxygen (O_2) is found in the lower atmosphere and gives life to all living beings through respiration. Ozone (O_3) is a poisonous gas with a very bad smell. It is found in the highest strata of the atmosphere. If we had to breathe ozone instead of oxygen, none of us would survive.

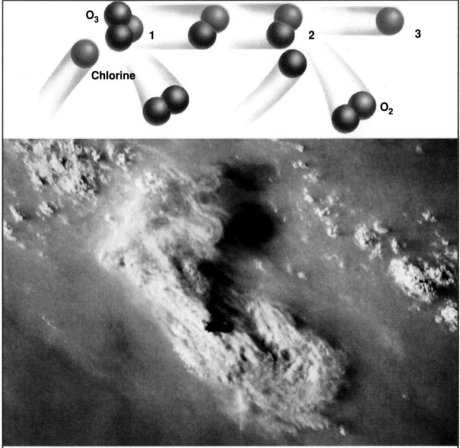

How does chlorine destroy ozone?
Chlorine reacts with ozone, producing an oxygen molecule and a hypochlorite ion (OCl-) (1). The ion reacts with an oxygen atom (2) to liberate free chlorine (3), which can react with and destroy another ozone molecule.[32]

The ozone is in the upper atmosphere, because there it serves a highly vital function for life. It forms a layer approximately 20 km above the atmosphere surrounding the earth like a belt. It absorbs the ultraviolet rays emitted by the sun, preventing them from reaching the earth at full intensity. Since ultraviolet rays have very high energy, their direct contact with the earth would cause everything on the earth to burn up, never allowing life to form. For this reason, the ozone layer serves as a protective shield in the atmosphere.

In order for life to exist on the earth, all living beings must be able to breathe and be protected from harmful sunrays. The one who forms this system is Allah, Who rules over each atom, each molecule. Without Allah's permission, no power whatsoever could bring these atoms together in different proportions as oxygen and ozone gas molecules.

Molecules We Taste and Smell

The senses of taste and smell are perceptions making man's world more beautiful. The pleasure derived from these senses has been a matter of interest since ancient times and it has been discovered only recently that these are caused by molecular interactions.

"Taste" and "smell" are only perceptions that are created by different molecules in our sense organs. For instance, the smells of food, drinks, or various fruits and flowers we see around us all consist of volatile molecules. So, how does this happen?

Volatile molecules like aroma of vanilla and aroma of rose reach the receptors located on the vibrating hairs in the nasal region called the epithelium and interact with those receptors. This interaction is perceived as smell in our brains. So far, seven different types of receptors have been identified in our nasal cavity, which is lined by a smelling membrane of 2-3 cm². Each one of these receptors corresponds to a basic smell. In the same way, there are four different types of chemical receptors in the front part of our tongue. These correspond to salty, sweet, sour and bitter tastes. Our brains perceive molecules arriving at the receptors of our sense organs as chemical signals.

It has been discovered how taste and smell are perceived and how they

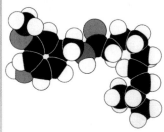

PIPERINE

Piperine is the active component of white and black pepper (the berries of the tropical vine *Piper nigrum*). Black pepper is obtained by allowing the unripe fruit to ferment and then drying it. White pepper is obtained by removing the skins and pulp of the ripe berries and drying the seeds.[33]

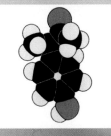

Para-HYDROXYPHENOL -2-BUTANONE ve IONONE

The mixture of these two molecules produces a very pleasant aroma. Butanone is the molecule chiefly responsible for the smell of ripe raspberries. The fresh new smell of the newly picked fruit is due partly to ionone, which is also responsible for the odours of sun-dried hay and violets. Ionone is the fragrant component of oil of violets.[34]

FURYLMETHANETHIOL

This molecule is one of those responsible for the aroma of coffee. The stimulating action of coffee is due to caffeine. The colour of roasted coffee beans seen left is largely due to the browning reaction that occurs when organic sub-stances containing nitrogen are heated. Temporarily trapped within the beans are the molecules responsible for flavour and stimulation.[35]

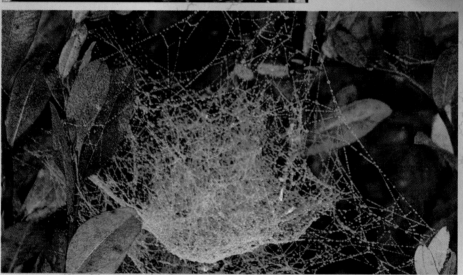

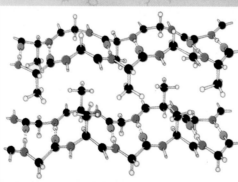

b-KERATIN

Silk, the common name of b-Keratin, is the solidified fluid excreted by a number of insects and spiders, the most valuable being the exu-dent of the silkworm, the caterpillar of the silk moth. It is a polypeptide made largely from glycine, alanine, and smaller amounts of other amino acids. b-Keratin molecules do not form a helix; instead they lie on top of each other to give ridged sheets of linked amino acids, with glycine appearing on only one side of the sheets. The sheets then stack one on top of the other. This planar structure is felt when you touch the smooth surface of silk.[36]

are formed, yet scientists have so far not been able to reach agreement as to why certain substances have a strong smell while some have less and why some taste good and some bad.

Think for a minute. We could be living in a world without any flavour or odour. Since we would have no idea about the concepts of taste and fragrance, it would not even occur to us to wish to possess these perceptions. However, it is not so. Out of the brown soil with a unique smell come hundreds of types of aromatic and delicious fruits, vegetables and flowers in thousands of colours, shapes and fragrances. Why then do these atoms, which, on one hand, come together in an extraordinary way to form matter, combine, on the other hand, to produce taste and smell? Although we often take them as granted and do not remember much what a great favour they are, they pleasantly contribute to our world as products of a magnificent artistry.

As for other living beings, some eat only grass and some different foodstuffs. Certainly, none of these smell good, or have a great taste. Even if they do, this does not mean much for these living beings as they do not have any consciousness in the sense that human beings have. We, too, could be feeding on a single type of nutrition like them. Have you ever thought how or-

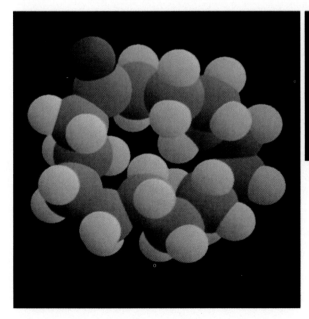

The picture above belongs to an evil-smelling molecule and the one on the left to an aromatic molecule. As we can see, what distinguishes bad odour from a pleasant odour is these small differences in a microcosm which is invisible to us.

dinary and tasteless your would life be if you had to eat a single type of food all your life and drink only water? Therefore, taste and smell, like all other blessings, are beauties Allah, possessor of infinite grace and bounty, gave man in return for nothing. The absence of even these two senses alone would make human life quite dull. In return for all these blessings given to him, what falls to man is to try to become a person with whom Allah would be pleased. In compensation for this attitude, his Lord promises him an eternal life, which is unlimitedly furnished with blessings far superior to those that are presented to us on the earth as samples of delights to come in the hereafter. However, the recompense of a life spent ungratefully, heedlessly, and neglectful of Allah, will certainly be a just one:

> **And when your Lord announced: "If you are grateful, I will certainly give you increase, but if you are ungrateful, My punishment is severe." (Surah Ibrahim: 7)**

How Do We Perceive Matter?

What we have told so far has revealed that what we call matter is not an entity having a specific colour, smell and form, as we believed it to be. What we imagine to be matter, that is our own body, our room, our home, and at large, the world and the whole universe, is in reality nothing but energy. What is it then that makes everything around us visible and touchable?

The reason why we perceive the things around us as matter is the collision of electrons in the orbital shells of atoms with photons, and the atoms' attracting and repelling each other.

You are not even touching the book that you think you hold in your hand right now… In truth, the atoms of your hand are repelling the atoms of the book and you feel a sense of touch depending on the intensity of this repulsion. As we mentioned while talking about the structure of atoms, they can come close to each other at most as much as the diameter of an atom. Besides, the only atoms that can come this close are those that react with each other. Therefore, when even atoms of the same substance can by no means touch each other, it is all the more impossible for us to touch the substance we hold, squeeze or lift with our hand. In fact, if we could come as close as possible to the object in our hand, we would be involved in a chemical reaction with that object. In this case, it would be impossible for a human being or another living being to survive even for a second. The living being would immediately react with the substance on which he stepped, sat or leaned, and be transformed into something else.

The final picture that emerges in this situation is extremely remarkable: we live in a world that is 99.95 % composed of a void filled with atoms consisting almost entirely of energy.[37] We actually never touch the things we say, "we touch and we hold". So, to what extent do we perceive the matter we see, hear or smell? Are these substances really as we see or hear them? Absolutely not. We had addressed this point when we talked about electrons and molecules. Remember, it is literally impossible for us to see the matter we believe to exist and see, because the phenomenon we call seeing comprises certain images formed in our brain by photons coming from the sun, or from another light source, hitting the matter, which absorbs a certain portion of the incoming light, and gives out the rest, which therefore is re-emitted from the matter and strikes our eyes. That is to say that the matter we see only consists of the information carried by photons that are reflected to our eye. So, how much of the data related to matter is conveyed to us by this information? We have no proof that the original forms of the matters existing outside are fully reflected to us.

CHAPTER 4

ATOMS THAT COME ALIVE

Up to here, we talked about atoms and how matter is created out of nothing. We said that atoms are the building blocks of everything whether animate or inanimate. It is important to note that atoms are building blocks of animate organisms as well as inanimate objects. Since atoms are inanimate particles, it is extremely astonishing for them to be the building blocks of living beings. This is also an issue evolutionists can never explain.

Just as it is impossible to imagine pieces of stone coming together to form living organisms, so is it impossible to imagine inanimate atoms by themselves coming together to form living organisms. Think about a lump of rock and a butterfly; one is inanimate, the other is animate. Yet, when we delve into their essences, we see that both are made up of the same sub-atomic particles.

The following example may be more explanatory regarding the impossibility of inanimate matter transforming by itself into animate matter: can aluminium fly? No. If we mix aluminium with plastic and gasoline, can it fly? Of course it still cannot. Only if we bring together these materials in a way so as to form an airplane, can they fly. So, what makes an airplane fly? Is it the wings? The engine? The pilot? None of these can fly by themselves. In fact, an airplane is manufactured by the assemblage in a special design of different pieces each of which has no ability to fly. The ability to fly is derived neither from aluminium, nor plastic, nor gasoline. The specifications of these substances are important, but the ability to fly can only be gained by bringing these substances together in a very special design. Living systems are no different. A living cell is formed by the arrangement of inanimate atoms in a very special design. Faculties of living cells, such as growth, reproduction and others, are results of perfect design rather than the properties of molecules. The design we find at this point is only Allah's creating the living from the dead:

Allah is He Who splits the seed and kernel. He brings forth the living from the dead, and produces the dead out of the living. That is Allah, so how are you perverted? (Surat al-An'am: 95)

Can materials – like the plastic, aluminium, and steel seen above – fly? No. They cannot fly even if they are all brought together in one place. An airplane is manufactured by the assemblage of different pieces, each of which has no ability to fly, in a special design. The ability to fly is derived neither from the aluminium, nor the plastic, nor the gasoline. The specifications of these substances are important, but the ability to fly can only be gained by bringing these substances together in a very special design. Living systems are no different. A living cell is formed by the arrangement of inanimate atoms in a very special design.

Only Allah, the Almighty and the Wise can give life to an inanimate substance, that is, create a living being. Living systems have such complex structures that it is still not fully understood how they operate despite the technological facilities available today.

However, there is a reality that is understood by the help of the science that made outstanding progress accompanied by a powerful technology that advanced in a devastating way in the 20th century. Living beings have extremely complex structures. When the theory of evolution was advanced in the middle of the 19th century, scientific research conducted with primitive microscopes had then created the impression that the cell was just a simple lump of matter. In the 20th century, however, observation and research made by the use of advanced instruments and electron microscopes revealed that the cell, which is the building block of living things, has an extremely complex structure that could only have been formed as a result of perfect design. Most importantly, this research showed that it is absolutely impossible for life to arise spontaneously out of inanimate matter. The source of life is life alone. This fact has been proved experimentally, too.[38] This is a problem evolutionists can never resolve. For this reason, instead of presenting scientific evidence, renowned evolutionary scientists, who are at a great impasse, tell tales which amount to nothing but window-dressing. They put forward totally illogical and unscientific claims that matter has a consciousness, ability and will of its own. Yet, they themselves do not believe these absurd tales either and they are eventually forced to confess that the main questions that need to be answered cannot be answered scientifically:

> There was once a time before our life, when the Earth was barren and utterly desolate. Our world is now overflowing with life. How did it come about? How, in the absence of life, were carbon-based organic molecules made? How did the first living things arise? How did life evolve to produce beings as elaborate and complex as we, able to explore the mystery of our own origins?[39]

> The outstanding evolutionary mystery now is how matter has originated and evolved, why it has taken its present form in the universe and on the earth, and why it is capable of forming itself into complex living sets of molecules.[40]

As the evolutionary scientist above confesses, the basic purpose of the theory of evolution is to deny that Allah created living beings. Although the Truth of Creation is obvious at every point of the universe and it has been definitively shown that each detail is the product of a design too perfect to have come about coincidentally, evolutionists turn a

How can you reject Allah, when you were dead and then He gave you life, then He will make you die and then give you life again, then you will be returned to Him? (Surat al-Baqara: 28)

93

blind eye to this fact and flounder in intellectual vicious circles.

Instead of believing this truth, however, evolutionary scientists prefer talking about the talents of dead matter and how inanimate bodies have transformed themselves into animate organisms. While closing their eyes to the truth, these scientists unknowingly put themselves to shame. It is obvious that claiming that atoms have some kind of a gift and that they use this gift to transform themselves into animate systems has nothing to do with reason.

After reading the example we will now quote, you will decide for yourself how realistic these irrational tales are. This is the scenario evolutionists claim, describing the transformation of inanimate and unconscious atoms into animate organisms, and most significantly, into people with high levels of consciousness and intelligence.

After the Big Bang, atoms, containing precisely balanced forces, somehow brought themselves into being. While some of the atoms, adequate in number to form the whole universe, formed the stars and the planets, and some others the earth. Some of the atoms making up the earth initially formed the land and later on, suddenly decided to form living beings! These atoms first transformed themselves into cells with highly complex structures and then produced copies of the cells they formed by splitting into two, after which they started speaking and hearing. Subsequently, these atoms trans-

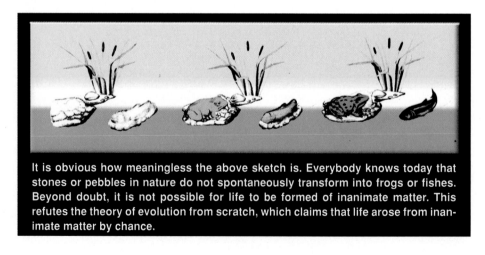

It is obvious how meaningless the above sketch is. Everybody knows today that stones or pebbles in nature do not spontaneously transform into frogs or fishes. Beyond doubt, it is not possible for life to be formed of inanimate matter. This refutes the theory of evolution from scratch, which claims that life arose from inanimate matter by chance.

WHILE ATOMS STUDY ATOMS

According to the evolutionary claim, atoms that formed by coincidence transformed into university professors and viewing themselves under electron microscopes, claimed that they were formed by chance. Unquestionably, such a claim is not convincing even to a small child.

formed into university professors viewing themselves under the electron microscope and claiming that they came into being coincidentally. Some atoms came together to form civil engineers who construct bridges and skyscrapers, while some others came together to manufacture satellites, space crafts and yet others specialised in the disciplines of physics, chemistry and biology. Atoms like carbon, magnesium, phosphorus, potassium and iron came together to form, instead of a dark mass, perfect brains of exceptional complexity, the secrets of which have not yet been fully unravelled. These brains started seeing 3-dimensional images with a perfect resolution never yet achieved by any technology. Some of the atoms formed comedians and laughed at the jokes comedians made. Again, some atoms composed music and enjoyed listening to it.

It is possible to prolong this story but let us stop here and run an experiment to show that such a story can never be realised. Let evolutionists put atoms, as much as required of all elements forming life, into a barrel. Let them add in this barrel whatever they think necessary for these atoms to uni-

te to form organic matter, and then let them wait. Let them wait for 100 years, 1000 years, and if necessary, for 100 million years transferring responsi-
bility to wait from father to son. Will a professor emerge out of this barrel
one day? Certainly not. Regardless of how long they wait, a professor will

not come out of this barrel. Not only will there be no professor, but not even a single living being would come out of this barrel. No birds, fishes, butterflies, apples, elephants, roses, strawberries, oranges, violets, trees, ants, honeybees, nor even a single mosquito would come out, because even if millions of pieces of organic matter came together, they would not spontaneously acquire the characteristics of a living being.

Now, let us see whether unconscious atoms can spontaneously form the DNA molecule, the cornerstone of life, and proteins.

DNA (Deoxyribonucleic Acid), which is located in the nucleus of the cell, contains the codes carrying the information of all organs and all characteristics of the body. This code is so complex that scientists were only able to translate it and then to a very limited extent as late as the 1940s. DNA, which contains all information on the living being it belongs to, is also able to reproduce itself. How a molecule formed by the assemblage of atoms can contain information and how it multiplies by copying itself remain one of the unanswered questions.

Proteins are the buildings blocks of living beings and they play a key role in many vital functions of the organism. For instance, haemoglobin transports oxygen everywhere in our body, antibodies render harmless microbes entering the body, and enzymes help us to digest the food we eat and

The DNA molecule that contains the complete information of living cells in a perfect coding system has an extremely complex structure. The flawless structure of this molecule utterly invalidates evolutionists' claim that it was formed by chance.

convert it into energy. The formulae found in our DNA enable the manufacture of 50,000 different types of proteins. As is obvious, proteins are highly crucial for the survival of a living being and the absence of even one of these proteins would make life impossible for that living being. It is scientifically impossible for DNA and proteins, each a giant molecule, to be formed spontaneously as a result of sheer coincidence.

> Everything in the heavens and the earth glorifies Allah. He is the Almighty, the All-Wise.
> The kingdom of the heavens and the earth belongs to Him. He gives life and causes to die. He has power over all things.
> (Surat al-Hadid: 1-2)

DNA is a series of nucleotides arranged in a special sequence. A protein is a series of amino acids arranged again in a special sequence. First of all, it is mathematically impossible for either DNA molecules or protein molecules that come in thousands of different types to sort out the appropriate sequences necessary for life by chance. Probabilistic calculations reveal that the probability of even the simplest protein molecules achieving the right sequence by chance is zero. (For more information, see the book *The Evolution Deceit* by Harun Yahya). In addition to this mathematical impossibility, there is also an important chemical obstacle to the coincidental formation of these molecules. If the relationship between DNA and protein were a result of time, chance, and natural processes, then there would be some sort of chemical tendency towards DNA and protein to react, as acids and bases have a great tendency to react. In that case, if chance had really played a role, sugar-acid, aminephosphoric acid, and a whole host of other natural chemical reactions would occur among any random fragments of DNA and protein and the living beings we see today would not form.

Does this natural tendency of DNA and protein fragments to react chemically, then, suggest that time, chance, and the laws of chemistry would eventually produce life from some mixture of these molecules? No. Just the opposite. The problem is that all these natural chemical reactions are the wrong reactions as far as living systems are concerned. Left to time, chance, and their own chemical tendencies, DNA and protein react in ways that destroy a living system and would prevent any postulated development of life.[41]

As seen, it is absolutely impossible for DNA and proteins, which can by no means form randomly, to be left uncontrolled to form life following their own formations. Jean Guitton, a contemporary philosopher, addressed this impossibility in his book titled *Dieu et la Science* (God and Science), stating that life could not have formed as a result of coincidences:

> Everything in the heavens and every creature on the earth prostrates to Allah, as do the angels. They are not puffed up with pride. They fear their Lord above them and do everything they are ordered to do. (Surat an-Nahl: 49-50)

> Following which 'coincidence' did certain atoms draw near each other to form the first molecules of amino acids? Again, through which coincidence did these molecules come together to form this extremely complex structure called DNA? I am asking this simple question just like the biological scientist François Jacob did: Who prepared the plans of the first DNA molecule to give the first message that led to the birth of the first living cell?

> If one is satisfied with assumptions involving coincidences, these questions – and many others – remain unanswered; this is why, for the last few years, the biologists began to change their views. Top researchers are not satisfied by re-telling Darwin's laws without thinking, parrot-fashion; they put forward new surprising theories. These are theories based on the idea that an organizing principle that is apparently superior to matter is involved in the process.[42]

As Jean Guitton stated, science has reached such a point, in the light of research and scientific discoveries made in the 20th century, that it has been scientifically established that Darwin's theory of evolution has no validity whatsoever. American biologist Michael Behe addresses this in his famous book *Darwin's Black Box*:

> Science has made enormous progress in understanding how the chemistry of life works, but the elegance and complexity of biological systems at the molecular level have paralysed science's attempt to explain their origins. There has been virtually no attempt to account for the origin of specific, complex biomolecular systems, much less any progress. Many scientists have gamely asserted that explanations are already in hand, or will be sooner or later, but no support for such assertions can be found in the professional science literature. More importantly, there are compelling reasons – based on the structure of the systems themselves – to think that a Darwinian explanation for the mechanisms of life will forever prove elusive.[43]

Just as the entire universe was created from nothing, so were living beings created from nothing. Just as only nothing can come into existence out of nothing by chance, inanimate matter cannot combine by chance to form living beings. Only Allah, Possessor of infinite power, infinite wisdom and infinite knowledge, has power to do all these:

> **Your Lord is Allah, Who created the heavens and the earth in six days and then settled Himself firmly on the Throne. He covers the day with the night, each pursuing the other urgently; and the sun and moon and stars are subservient to His command. Both creation and command belong to Him. Blessed be Allah, the Lord of all the worlds. (Surat al-A'raf: 54)**

CHAPTER 5

POWER OF THE ATOM

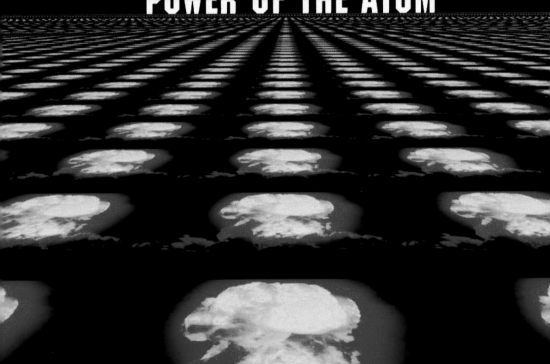

We now know how atoms, the building blocks of the whole universe and everything therein, animate-inanimate, form matter in an extraordinary way. As we have examined, these extremely minute particles have a perfect organisation within themselves. Yet, the miraculous aspect of the atom does not end there; the atom also houses tremendous energy.

This power hidden in the atom is so great that its discovery has enabled man to build huge canals uniting oceans, dig through mountains, produce artificial climates and accomplish many similar useful projects. However, while the power hidden in the atom serves humanity on one hand, it poses an extremely great danger for humanity on the other hand. So much so that by the misuse of this power, tens of thousands of people lost their lives in a very short time– a few seconds – at Hiroshima and Nagasaki during World War II. In recent years, an accident that took place in the Chernobyl nuclear power plant in Russia caused the death or injury of a great number of people.

Before giving detailed information on the disasters the power of the atom caused in Hiroshima, Nagasaki and Chernobyl, let us take a short look at the nature of this power in the atom and how it is released.

Power Hidden in the Nucleus

In the chapter titled "The Formation Adventure of the Atom", we had said the force keeping the protons and neutrons together in the atomic nucleus is "the strong nuclear force". The enormous power of nuclear energy is revealed by the liberation of a tiny part of this force in the nucleus. The magnitude of this energy varies depending on the type of the element, because the number of protons and neutrons in the nucleus of each element is different. As the nucleus grows, the number of neutrons and protons and the magnitude of the force bonding them to each other increase. It is extremely difficult to release this force that is responsible for keeping protons and neutrons together in a large nucleus. As the particles grow more distant from each other, they, just like a taut bow, try to come together with greater force.

Before going into the details of this force, let us think it over. How can

Neutron

Uranium 235

such an enormous force
fit in such a small place? This
is such a force that it has been
discovered after years of research
conducted by thousands of people.
When it is not interfered with, it does not do
any harm to anyone, yet, with the intervention
of man, it may at any time become a force killing
millions.

Two technical processes called "fission" and "fusion" release this extraordinary force in the nucleus of the atom, which may endanger the lives of millions of people. Although these reactions at first seem to take place in the nucleus of the atom, they actually involve all the components of the atom. The reaction known as fission is a nuclear reaction in which an atomic nucleus splits into fragments, and the reaction called fusion is the bringing together of two nuclei by a great force. In either reaction, a tremendous amount of energy is released.

Fission

Fission is a nuclear reaction in which the atomic nucleus, which is held together by the strongest force in the universe, the "Strong Nuclear Force", splits into fragments. The main material used in fission experiments is "uranium" because the uranium atom is one of the heaviest. In other words, there are plenty of protons and neutrons in its nucleus.

In fission experiments, scientists shot a neutron at the uranium nucleus at great velocity. They faced a very interesting situation. After the neutron was absorbed by the uranium's nucleus, the uranium nucleus had become very unstable. The nucleus' being "unstable" means the formation of a diffe-

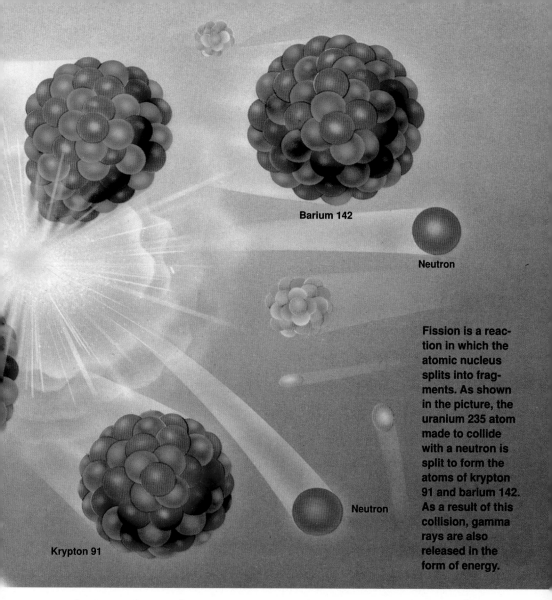

Barium 142

Neutron

Krypton 91

Neutron

Fission is a reaction in which the atomic nucleus splits into fragments. As shown in the picture, the uranium 235 atom made to collide with a neutron is split to form the atoms of krypton 91 and barium 142. As a result of this collision, gamma rays are also released in the form of energy.

rence between the numbers of protons and neutrons in the nucleus, resulting in an imbalance in its structure. Therefore, the nucleus starts splitting into fragments while emitting a certain amount of energy to eliminate this imbalance. The nucleus, under the impact of the energy released, starts ejecting the components it contains at great velocity.

Considering the results these experiments yielded, neutrons were accelerated and uranium was bombarded with neutrons in special environments called "reactors". However, uranium is bombarded with neutrons according to a very fine measure, not randomly, because any neutron bombarding the uranium atom has to hit the uranium immediately and at the desired point. That is why these experiments are conducted taking every probability into consideration. The amount of the uranium to be used, the amount of the neutrons used to bombard the uranium, and the duration and speed at which the neutrons will bombard the uranium should all be very precisely calculated.

After all these calculations are made and the appropriate setting is prepared, the nucleus is bombarded with neutrons in such a way that they penetrate the nuclei of the atoms in the uranium. It is sufficient that the nucleus of at least one of the atoms in this mass is split in two. In this division, an average of two or three neutrons are sent out from the mass of the nucleus at great velocity and high energy. Neutrons that are released start a chain reaction by colliding with other uranium nuclei within the mass. Each newly split nucleus behaves like the initial uranium nucleus. Thus, a chain of nuclear reactions starts. A large number of uranium nuclei are split into fragments as a result of these chain reactions, causing an enormous amount of energy to be released.

It was these nuclei divisions that have caused the Hiroshima and Nagasaki disasters, causing the death of tens of thousands of people. At the moment of the detonation of the atomic bomb dropped on Hiroshima by the United States in 1945 during World War II, and in its aftermath, approximately 100,000 people died. Another atom bomb dropped on Nagasaki by America three days after the Hiroshima disaster caused the death of another 40,000 people right at the moment of detonation. While the power released by the nuclei caused the death of many people, it also destroyed a very large residential area, and gave rise to many irreparable genetic and physiological disorders in the remaining residents of that area, due to the radiation released, which was to affect generations to come.

If our earth, the whole atmosphere, everything animate and inanimate including us, are composed of atoms, what prevents atoms from being involved in nuclear reactions like the ones in Hiroshima and Nagasaki, that could occur anytime and anywhere?

The neutrons are created in such a way that, when they are free in nature – without being linked to a nucleus – they are subjected to a decompositi-on called "beta disintegration". Because of this disintegration, no neutrons wander freely in nature. Therefore, neutrons that are to be used in nuclear reactions must be obtained through artificial methods.

This makes clear that, Allah, the Creator of the entire universe, created everything with a precise measure. If neutrons had not decomposed in the free state, the earth would be nothing but an uninhabitable spherical celesti-al body where endless nuclear reactions took place. Allah created the atom along with this colossal power within it and keeps this power under control in a phenomenal way.

Fusion

Nuclear fusion, just the contrary of fission, is the process of bringing to-gether two light nuclei to form a heavier nucleus and using the bonding energy thus released. However, to achieve this in a controlled fashion is very difficult. This is because nuclei carry positive electrical charges and repel each other very strongly if forced to come together. Therefore, a force strong enough to overcome the repulsive force between them must be used to make them fuse. This required kinetic energy is equivalent to a temperature of 20-30 million degrees.[44] This is an extraordinarily high temperature and no so-lid material used to contain the particles that will be involved in a fusion re-action can tolerate this temperature. That is, there is no mechanism on earth that is able to realise this fusion except the heat of the atomic bomb.

Fusion reactions take place in the sun all the time. The heat and light co-ming from the sun is the result of hydrogen being fused into helium and energy being released in place of the matter lost during this conversion. Each second, the sun converts 564 million tons of hydrogen to 560 million tons of helium. The remaining 4 million tons of matter is converted into energy. This tremendous event producing the solar energy that is extremely vital for life on our planet, has continued for millions of years without pause. This may bring to our minds such a question: If such a great amount of matter as 4 mil-lion tons is lost in the sun each second, when will the sun be fully consu-med?

Nuclear fusion, just the contrary of fission, is the process of bringing together two light nuclei to form a heavier nucleus and using the bonding energy thus released. The nuclei in the stars fuse when they collide. New nuclei are thus formed, and neutrinos, positrons, neutrons, protons and other sub-atomic particles are released as energy. The source of the great energy in the stars is these nuclear fusions.

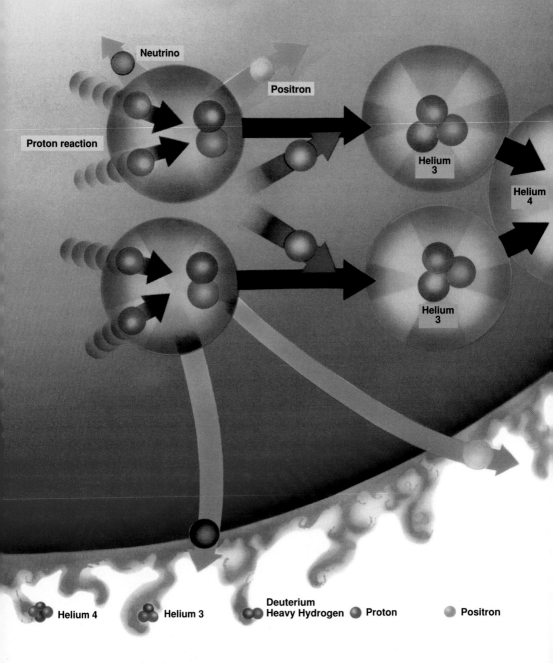

Neutrino

Positron

Proton reaction

Helium 3

Helium 4

Helium 3

Helium 4   Helium 3   Deuterium Heavy Hydrogen   Proton   Positron

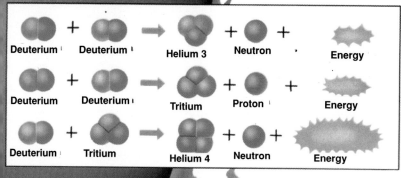

Proton

The sun loses 4 million tons of matter per second, 240 million tons per minute. If we assume that the sun has been producing energy at this rate for 3 billion years, the mass it has lost during this period would be 400,000 million times million tons, which is equal to one 5,000th of the current total mass of the sun. This amount is like one gram of sand being lost out of a 5 kilogram rock in 3 billion years. As this makes clear, the mass of the sun is so enormous that a very long time has to pass before it is finished.

Man has only discovered the composition of the sun and the events taking place inside it this century. Earlier, no one ever knew about phenomena such as nuclear explosions, fission or fusion. Nobody knew how the sun produced energy. Yet, while man was unaware of all these, the sun always continued to be the energy source of the earth and life, for millions of years with this incredible mechanism.

Now, the really curious thing is that our earth has been placed at such an exact distance from the sun – a source of energy possessing an enormous mass – that it is neither exposed to its scorching, destructive power, nor deprived of the useful energy it provides. In the same way, the sun, which possesses such enormous power and energy, is created at the distance, with the power and the size which are perfect for all life on earth, and foremost, man.

This gigantic mass and the incredible nuclear reactions occurring in it have been carrying on their activities for millions of years in perfect harmony with the earth and in the most controlled manner. To understand what an extraordinary, controlled and balanced system this is, it is good enough to remember that man is incapable of controlling even one simple nuclear power plant he has established. No scientist, no technological equipment was able to prevent the nuclear accident that occurred in the Chernobyl reactor in Russia in 1986. It is said that the impact of this nuclear accident will endure for 30-40 years. Although scientists have covered around the contaminated sections of the reactor with enormously thick concrete to prevent further damage, it was later reported that there were leaks from the concrete. Let alone nuclear explosions, even nuclear leaks are extremely dangerous for human life, and science is helpless against this threat.

At this point, we stand facing Allah's endless power and His sovereignty over each particle (atom) in the universe and the sub-atomic particles inside this particle (protons, neutrons…). Allah's power and sovereignty over the beings He creates are stated in a verse as follows:

Hundreds of thousands of people lost their lives in a few seconds through the liberation of the enormous power hidden in the nucleus of the atom.

The detonation left behind permanent traces.

The nuclear accident that occurred in the Chernobyl reactor in Russia in 1986 had permanent effects on human beings and all other animate things. Scientists say these effects will last another 30-40 years. Measures to prevent nuclear leaks have not been helpful. A study is underway for the elimination of the harmful effects of radiation.

You do not engage in any matter or recite any of the Qur'an or do any action without Our witnessing you while you are occupied with it. Not even the smallest speck eludes your Lord, either on earth or in heaven. Nor is there anything smaller than that, or larger, which is not in a Clear Book. (Surah Yunus: 61)

Effects of the Atomic Bomb: Hiroshima and Nagasaki

The atomic bombs dropped in the final year of World War II have revealed to the whole world the tremendous power hidden in the atom. Both bombs caused hundreds of thousands of people to lose their lives and inflicted lifelong physical damage on many of the survivors.

Let us see how the enormous power inside the atom, causing the deaths of hundreds of thousands of people in a few seconds, is released second by second:

- The moment of explosion...

Let us assume that an atomic bomb explodes at an altitude of 2,000 m as it did in Hiroshima and Nagasaki. The neutrons bombarding the uranium and which split the first atoms into fragments creates chain reactions within the mass as mentioned before. In other words, the neutrons thrown out from the first fragmented nuclei hit other nuclei and split these new nuclei as well. Thus, all nuclei are rapidly fragmented in a chain reaction and the explosion

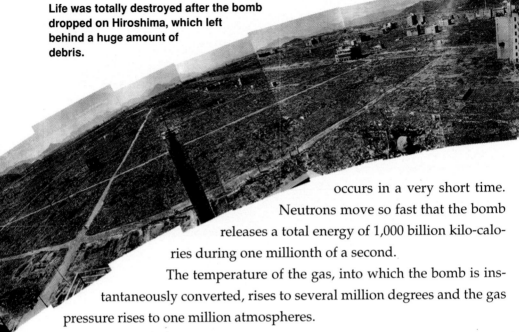

Life was totally destroyed after the bomb dropped on Hiroshima, which left behind a huge amount of debris.

occurs in a very short time. Neutrons move so fast that the bomb releases a total energy of 1,000 billion kilo-calories during one millionth of a second.

The temperature of the gas, into which the bomb is instantaneously converted, rises to several million degrees and the gas pressure rises to one million atmospheres.

- One thousandth of a second after the explosion...

The diameter of the detonated mass of gas increases and various rays are emitted. These radiations form the "initial flash" of the explosion. This flash may cause full blindness in anyone standing within an area having a diameter of tens of kilometres. This flash is hundreds of times stronger than that emitted from the surface of the sun (per surface unit). The time elapsed since the outset of the explosion is so short that people close to the explosion site cannot even find time to close their eyes.

The pressure of the shock causes heavy damage indoors. Power transmission towers, two-piece bridges and skyscrapers built from glass-steel are also damaged. In the close surroundings of the explosion, a great amount of powder-like fine dust is raised.

- 2 seconds after the explosion...

The flashing mass and the air surrounding it form a fireball. The heat radiated from this fireball, whose surface is still extremely hot and which glows like the sun and even more, is powerful enough to ignite all combustible matter within an area of 4-5 kilometres in diameter. The radiance of the

Radiation debris was spread over a very large area as a result of the strong winds formed after the explosion, and left behind a picture as if everything had been covered by a layer of ash.

fireball may cause irreparable damage to the sense of vision. At this moment, a shock wave moving at very great speed develops around the fireball.

- 6 seconds after the explosion...

At this point, the shock wave hits the earth and causes the first mechanical damage. The wave creates powerful air pressure, the intensity of which decreases as one goes farther from the centre of the explosion. Even around 1.5 km away from this point, the added pressure is twice as strong as normal atmospheric pressure. The chance of people staying alive at this pressure is 1%.

- 13 seconds after the explosion...

The shock wave diffuses along the surface of the earth and it is followed by the explosion created by the repositioning of the air sent by the fireball. This explosion diffuses along the earth at a speed of 300-400 km per hour.

In the meantime, the fireball has cooled down and its volume has decreased. Being lighter than air, it starts to rise. This upward motion causes the direction of wind on the earth to reverse and causes a strong wind to start blowing towards the centre, even though it was initially blowing outwards from the centre of the explosion.

- 30 seconds after the explosion...

As the fireball rises, its spherical shape is distorted and it takes the appearance of a mushroom.

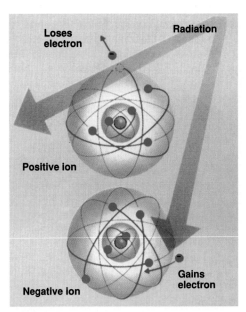

Radiation may result in very serious damage, by forming positive ions when it hits and removes the electrons on the outer surface of the atom. Electrons form negative ions by bonding to other neutral atoms.

2 minutes after the explosion...

The mushroom shaped cloud has now reached an altitude of 12,000 metres. This is the lower limit of the stratospheric layer of the atmosphere. The winds blowing at this altitude cause the mushroom shaped cloud to disperse and the components of the cloud (mostly radioactive remains) to scatter into the atmosphere. As these radioactive remains consist of very tiny particles, they may rise to higher layers in the atmosphere. Before falling on the earth, these remains may be made to travel several times around the earth by the winds blowing in the upper layers of the atmosphere. Thus, radioactive remains may be dispersed all over the world.

Radiation Emitted By the Atom

Radiation consists of gamma rays, neutrons, electrons and similar subatomic particles moving at very high speeds such as 200,000 km per second. These particles may easily penetrate the human body and harm the cells forming the body. This damage may cause a fatal cancer or, if it takes place in reproductive cells, it may give rise to genetic disorders that will influence generations to come. Therefore, the results of a radioactive particle hitting a human being are very serious.

Radiation released in atomic explosions affects living beings either directly or through the products of radioactive decay that emerge during the explosion.

As one of these particles or rays travels at high speed in matter, it colli-

Those who disbelieve say, 'The Hour will never come.' Say: 'Yes, by my Lord, it certainly will come!' He is the Knower of the Unseen, Whom not even the weight of the smallest particle eludes, either in the heavens or in the earth; nor is there anything smaller or larger than that which is not in a Clear Book. (Surah Saba': 3)

des very strongly with atoms or molecules that get in its way. This collision may be a disaster for the delicate structure of the cell. The cell may die, or, even if it recovers, it may start to grow in an uncontrolled fashion – which is cancer – perhaps weeks, months, or years later.

Radiation is very intense in an area of 1,000 metres in diameter around the centre of the explosion. Those who survive other fatal factors lose almost all white cells in their blood, wounds appear on their skins, and all of them die because of haemorrhages in a short period of time from a few days up to two or three weeks. The effect of radiation on those farther from the point of explosion varies. Those who are exposed to these harmful rays emitted by the fireball at distances of 13, 16, and 22 km suffer from third, second, and first degree burns respectively. Digestive problems and haemorrhages are experienced less, but real disorders appear later: hair loss, skin burns, anaemia, sterility, miscarriages, giving birth to crippled or deformed babies. In these cases, too, death is possible within a period from ten days to three months. Even years later, sight disorders, leukaemia and radiation cancer may develop. One of the greatest dangers of hydrogen bomb explosions (another nuclear bomb of enormous destructive power caused by the fusion of the nuclei of various hydrogen isotopes in the formation of helium nuclei) is the entrance of radioactive dust into the body through respiration, digestion and the skin. This dust causes the above-mentioned disorders depending on the degree of contamination.

All these are caused by atoms, which we cannot even see with our eyes. Atoms can form life just as they can destroy it. This property of the atom shows us very clearly how helpless we are and how superior is Allah's power.

CONCLUSION

With your body made up of atoms, you are breathing atoms in the air, eating atoms in food and drinking atoms of water. What you see is nothing other than the collision of electrons of the atoms in your eye with photons. And what about what you feel by touch? The sensations are simply formed by atoms in your skin repelling atoms of objects.

Indeed, almost everyone knows today that his body, the universe, the world, in short, everything consists of atoms. Yet, perhaps, most people so far never thought about what kind of a system the entity we call the atom has. Or, even if they did, they did not feel the need to investigate it, because they always thought this concerns physicists alone.

Man, however, lives entwined within this perfect system throughout his life. This is such a system that every one of the trillions of atoms forming the armchair on which we sit has an order about which a book could be written. It takes pages to tell the formation, the system and the power of a single atom. As the technology advances and our knowledge of the universe increases, these pages also increase.

How then did this order form? It cannot be that the particles scattered around after the Big Bang have formed the atom with a sudden decision, and then an appropriate environment was formed by chance, and these atoms have transformed into matter. It is certainly impossible to explain such a system by "chance". Everything you see around you, and even the air you cannot see, consist of atoms, and there is a very complex traffic between these atoms.

Who then can direct the traffic between the atoms? Can it be you? If you think that your body consists of atoms alone, then which one of your atoms directs which, and which atom directs what? Do the atoms of your brain that are no different from other atoms control the others? If we assume that the atoms of your brain are directors, then we have to answer these questions:

* If all atoms forming the brain are directors, how and based on what do they make their decisions?

* How do trillions of atoms forming the brain cooperate?

* Why does not a single atom out of trillions of them oppose the decision that is taken?

* How do the atoms communicate with each other?

Considering the above questions, it is obviously an illogical deduction to say that all of the trillions of atoms forming the brain are directors.

So, can it be correct to think that only one of these trillions of atoms is the director and the others are its followers? If we believe a single atom to be the director, then the questions that come to the mind are:

* Which atom is the director and who elected this atom?

* Where in the brain is this atom?

* What is the difference of this atom from the others?

* Why do the other atoms obey this atom unconditionally?

Before answering these questions, let us state one more thing: the supposed director atom is also made up of other particles. Why and under what pretext do these particles come together to form this director atom? Who controls these particles? Since there is another will directing these particles, how right would it be to defend that this atom is the director?

At this point, the claim that one of the atoms forming our brain may be the director atom is inevitably disproved. How do the countless number of atoms in the universe continue their existence in full harmony, while people, animals, plants, earth, air, water, objects, planets, space, and everything else are made of atoms? Which one of these countless atoms can be the director when it itself is made up of many sub-particles? To make such a claim or to attribute everything to chance and to deny the being of Allah, Who created all the worlds, is only **"rejecting those signs in iniquity and arrogance in spite of their own certainty about them."** (Surat an-Naml: 14)

Just think: a human being, who is made up of the arrangement of atoms in various combinations, is born, is fed with atoms and grows up with atoms. He then reads books made of atoms in a building made of atoms. Later, he receives a diploma composed of atoms that says "nuclear engineer" on it. Yet, he can still come and deliver speeches such as "these atoms have come together as a result of sheer coincidence, and the extraordinary system within them has formed by chance". If this is so, where does he derive the consciousness, will and intelligence to deliver this speech?

In almost every page of this book, we saw repeatedly that it is impossible for the atom making up every animate or inanimate thing in the universe, to be itself formed by chance. What we will say to those who, despite all we have told, still think that this phenomenon has come about by "chance" or taken its present form through the mechanism of "trial and error" will be no different from what the prophet Ibrahim, peace be upon him, said to the disbelievers:

> **What about the one who argued with Ibrahim about his Lord, on the basis that Allah had given him sovereignty? Ibrahim said, 'My Lord is He who gives life and causes to die.' He said, 'I too give life and cause to die.' Ibrahim said, 'Allah makes the sun come from the East. Make it come from the West.' And the disbeliever was dumbfounded. Allah does not guide wrongdoing people. (Surat al-Baqara: 258)**

They said 'Glory be to You!
We have no knowledge except what
You have taught us. You are the All-Knowing,
the All-Wise.'
(Surat al-Baqara: 32)

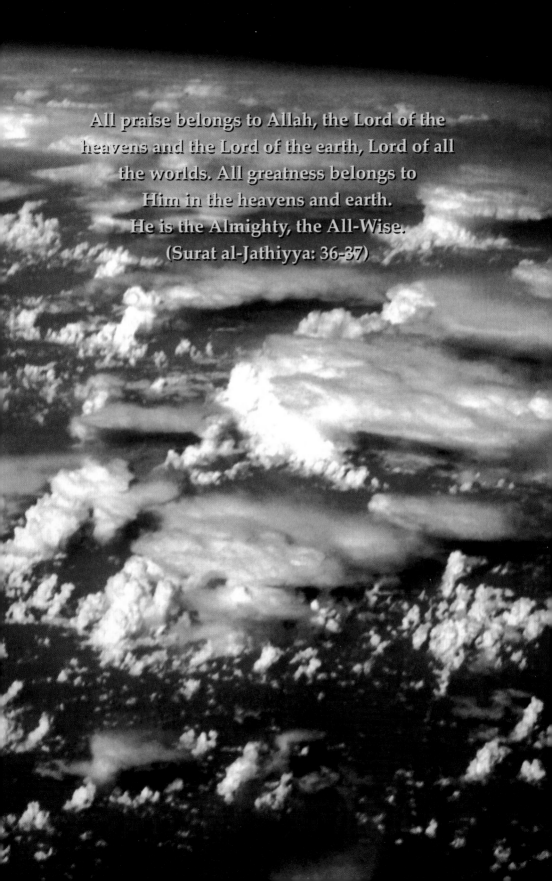

All praise belongs to Allah, the Lord of the
heavens and the Lord of the earth, Lord of all
the worlds. All greatness belongs to
Him in the heavens and earth.
He is the Almighty, the All-Wise.
(Surat al-Jathiyya: 36-37)

NOTES

1. David Filkin, *Stephen Hawking's Universe: The Cosmos Explained*, Basic Books, October 1998, pp. 85-86
2. *Stephen Hawking's A Brief History of Time A Reader's Companion* (Edited by Stephen Hawking; prepared by Gene Stone), New York, Bantam Books, 1982, p. 62-63
3. Henry Margenau, Roy Abraham Vargesse, *Cosmos, Bios, Theos*, La Salla IL: Open Court Publishing, 1992, p. 241
4. H. P. Lipson, "A Physicist Looks at Evolution", *Physics Bulletin*, vol. 138, 1980, p. 138
5. Taşkın Tuna, *Uzayın Sırları* (The Secrets of Space), Boğaziçi Yayınları, p.185
6. Colin A. Ronan, *The Universe Explained*, The Earth-Dwellers's Guide to the Mysteries of Space, Henry Holt and Company, pp. 178-179
7. Taşkın Tuna, *Uzayın Sırları* (The Secrets of Space), Boğaziçi Yayınları, p.186
8. Steven Weinberg, *The First Three Minutes, A Modern View of the Origin of the Universe*, Basic Books, June 1993, p. 87
9. Stephen W. Hawking, *A Brief History of Time,* Bantam Books, April 1988, p. 121
10. Hugh Ross, *The Creator and the Cosmos, How Greatest Scientific Discoveries of the Century Reveal God*, Colorado: NavPress, Revised Edition, 1995, p. 76
11. Michael Denton, *Nature's Destiny:How The Laws of Biology Reveal Purpose in the Universe*, The New York: The Free Press, 1998, pp. 12-13
12. Paul Davies, *The Accidental Universe*, Cambridge: Cambridge University Press, 1982, Foreword
13. Jean Guitton, *Dieu et La Science: Vers Le Métaréalisme*, Paris: Grasset, 1991, p. 62
14. Jean Guitton, *Dieu et La Science: Vers Le Métaréalisme*, Paris: Grasset, 1991, p. 62
15. Jean Guitton, *Dieu et La Science: Vers Le Métaréalisme*, Paris: Grasset, 1991, p. 62
16. Ümit Şimşek, *Atom* (The Atom), Yeni Asya Yayınları, p.7
17. Taşkın Tuna, *Uzayın Ötesi* (Beyond Space), Boğaziçi Yayınları, 1995, p. 53
18. Jean Guitton, *Dieu et La Science: Vers Le Métaréalisme*, Paris: Grasset, 1991, p. 62
19. Taşkın Tuna, *Uzayın Ötesi* (Beyond Space), Boğaziçi Yayınları, 1995, p. 52
20. David Filkin, *Stephen Hawking's Universe: The Cosmos Explained*, Basic Books, October 1998, pp. 143-144
21. Richard Feynman, *The Character of Physical Law*, The M.I.T. Press, March 1967, p. 128
22. Richard Feynman, *The Character of Physical Law*, The M.I.T. Press, March 1967, p. 129
23. Jean Guitton, *Dieu et La Science: Vers Le Métaréalisme*, Paris: Grasset, 1991, p. 5
24. Martin Sherwood & Christine Sulton, *The Physical World*, Oxford University Press, 1988, p. 81
25. Martin Sherwood & Christine Sulton, *The Physical World*, Oxford University Press, 1988, p. 82
26. Martin Sherwood & Christine Sulton, *The Physical World*, Oxford University Press, 1988, p. 79
27. L. Vlasov, D. Trifonov, *107 Stories About Chemistry*, 1977, p. 117
28. L. Vlasov, D. Trifonov, *107 Stories About Chemistry*, 1977, p. 118
29. David Burnie, *Life*, Eyewitness Science, London: Dorling Kindersley, 1996, p.8
30. Nevil V. Sidgwick, *The Chemical Elements and Their Compounds*, vol.1, Oxford: Oxford University Press, 1950, p.490
31. Martin Sherwood & Christine Sulton, *The Physical World*, Oxford University Press, 1988, p. 30
32. *Structure of Matter*, The Time Inc. Book Company, 1992, p. 76
33. P.W. Atkins, *Molecules*, Scientific American Library, p. 115
34. P.W. Atkins, *Molecules*, Scientific American Library, p. 128
35. P.W. Atkins, *Molecules*, Scientific American Library, p. 130
36. P.W. Atkins, *Molecules*, Scientific American Library, p. 93
37. Taşkın Tuna, *Uzayın Ötesi* (Beyond Space), Boğaziçi Yayınları, 1995, p. 166
38. Henry M. Morris, Impact No. 111, Septemberl 1982
39. Carl Sagan, *Cosmos*, Random House, April 1983, p. 24
40. C.D. Darlington, *Evolution for Naturalists*, (NY, John Wiley, 1980) p. 15
41. Dr. Gary Parker, Impact No: 62, August 1978
42. Jean Guitton, *Dieu et La Science: Vers Le Métaréalisme*, Paris: Grasset, 1991, p. 38
43. Michael Behe, *Darwin's Black Box*, Free Press, 1996, p.x
44. Théma Larousse, *Tematik Ansiklopedi Bilim ve Teknoloji* (Encyclopedia of Science and Technology), p. 300

Also by Harun Yahya

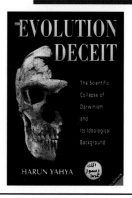

Many people think that Darwin's Theory of Evolution is a proven fact. Contrary to this conventional wisdom, recent developments in science completely disprove the theory. The only reason Darwinism is still foisted on people by means of a worldwide propaganda campaign lies in the ideological aspects of the theory. All secular ideologies and philosophies try to provide a basis for themselves by relying on the theory of evolution.

This book clarifies the scientific collapse of the theory of evolution in a way that is detailed but easy to understand. It reveals the frauds and distortions committed by evolutionists to "prove" evolution. Finally it analyzes the powers and motives that strive to keep this theory alive and make people believe in it.

Anyone who wants to learn about the origin of living things, including mankind, needs to read this book.

238 PAGES WITH 166 PICTURES IN COLOUR

One of the purposes why the Qur'an was revealed is to summon people to think about creation and its works. When a person examines his own body or any other living thing in nature, the world or the whole universe, in it he sees a great design, art, plan and intelligence. All this is evidence proving Allah's being, unit, and eternal power.

For Men of Understanding was written to make the reader see and realise some of the evidence of creation in nature. Many living miracles are revealed in the book with hundreds of pictures and brief explanations.

288 PAGES WITH 467 PICTURES IN COLOUR

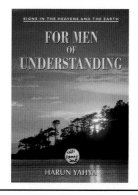

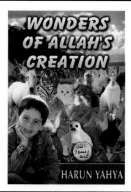

Children!

Have you ever asked yourself questions like these: How did our earth come into existence? How did the moon and sun come into being? Where were you before you were born? How did oceans, trees, animals appear on earth? How do your favourite fruits –bananas, cherries, plums– with all their bright colours and pleasant scents grow in black soil? How does a little tiny bee know how to produce delicious honey? How can it build a honeycomb with such astonishingly regular edges? Who was the first human being? Your mom gave birth to you. Yet the first human being could not have had parents. So, how did he come into existence?" In this book you will find the true answers to these questions.

144 PAGES WITH 282 PICTURES IN COLOUR

People who are oppressed, who are tortured to death, innocent babies, those who cannot afford even a loaf of bread, who must sleep in tents or even in streets in cold weather, those who are massacred just because they belong to a certain tribe, women, children, and old people who are expelled from their homes because of their religion… Eventually, there is only one solution to the injustice, chaos, terror, massacres, hunger, poverty, and oppression: the morals of the Qur'an.

208 PAGES WITH 276 PICTURES IN COLOUR

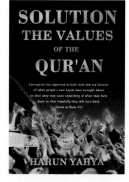

Never plead ignorance of Allah's evident existence, that everything was created by Allah, that everything you own was given to you by Allah for your subsistence, that you will not stay so long in this world, of the reality of death, that the Qur'an is the Book of truth, that you will give account for your deeds, of the voice of your conscience that always invites you to righteousness, of the existence of the hereafter and the day of account, that hell is the eternal home of severe punishment, and of the reality of fate.
112 PAGES WITH 74 PICTURES IN COLOUR

One of the major reasons why people feel a profound sense of attachment to life and cast religion aside is the assumption that life is eternal. Forgetting that death is likely to put an end to this life at any time, man simply believes that he can enjoy a perfect and happy life. Yet he evidently deceives himself. The world is a temporary place specially created by Allah to test man. That is why, it is inherently flawed and far from satisfying man's endless needs and desires. Each and every attraction existing in the world eventually wears out, becomes corrupt, decays and finally disappears. This is the never-changing reality of life.
This book explains this most important essence of life and leads man to ponder the real place to which he belongs, namely the Hereafter.
224 PAGES WITH 144 PICTURES IN COLOUR

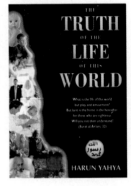

Many societies that rebelled against the will of Allah or regarded His messengers as enemies were wiped off the face of the earth completely... All of them were destroyed–some by a volcanic eruption, some by a disastrous flood, and some by a sand storm...
Perished Nations examines these penalties as revealed in the verses of the Quran and in light of archaeological discoveries.
149 PAGES WITH 73 PICTURES IN COLOUR

Darwin said: "If it could be demonstrated that any complex organ existed, which could not possibly have been formed by numerous, successive, slight modifications, my theory would absolutely break down." When you read this book, you will see that Darwin's theory has absolutely broken down, just as he feared it would.
A thorough examination of the feathers of a bird, the sonar system of a bat or the wing structure of a fly reveal amazingly complex designs. And these designs indicate that they are created flawlessly by Allah.
208 PAGES WITH 302 PICTURES IN COLOUR

The evidence of Allah's creation is present everywhere in the universe. A person comes across many of these proofs in the course of his daily life; yet if he does not think deeply, he may wrongly consider them to be trivial details. In fact in every creature there are great mysteries to be pondered.
These millimeter-sized animals that we frequently come across but don't care much about have an excellent ability for organization and specialization that is not to be matched by any other being on earth. These aspects of ants create in one a great admiration for Allah's superior power and unmatched creation.
165 PAGES WITH 104 PICTURES IN COLOUR

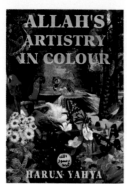

Colours, patterns, spots, even lines of each living being existing in nature have a meaning. For some species, colours serve as a communication tool; for others, they are a warning against enemies. Whatever the case, these colours are essential for the well-being of living beings. An attentive eye would immediately recognise that not only the living beings, but also everything in nature are just as they should be. Furthermore, he would realise that everything is given to the service of man: the comforting blue colour of the sky, the colourful view of flowers, the bright green trees and meadows, the moon and stars illuminating the world in pitch darkness together with innumerable beauties surrounding man...

160 PAGES WITH 215 PICTURES IN COLOUR

In the Qur'an, there is an explicit reference to the "second coming of the Jesus to the world" which is heralded in a hadith. The realisation of some information revealed in the Qur'an about Jesus can only be possible by Jesus' second coming...

Have you ever thought that you were non-existent before you were born and suddenly appeared on Earth? Have you ever thought that the peel of a banana, melon, watermelon or an orange each serve as a quality package preserving the fruit's odour and taste? Man is a being to which Allah has granted the faculty of thinking. Yet a majority of people fail to employ this faculty as they should... The purpose of this book is to summon people to think in the way they should and to guide them in their efforts to think.

128 PAGES WITH 137 PICTURES IN COLOUR

Dear kids, while reading this book you will see how God has created all the creatures in the most beautiful way and how every one of them show us His endless beauty, power and knowledge. The World of Animals is also available in French.

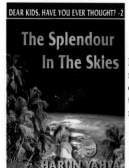

Have you ever thought about the vast dimensions of the universe we live in? As you read this book, you will see that our universe and all the living things therein are created in the most perfect way by our Creator, God. You will learn that God created the sun, the moon, our world, in short, everything in the universe so that we may live in it in the most peaceful and happy way.

MEDIA PRODUCTS BASED ON
THE WORKS OF HARUN YAHYA

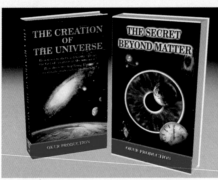

HARUN YAHYA ON THE INTERNET

www.harunyahya.com
www.creationofuniverse.com
www.evolutiondeceit.com
www.jesuswillreturn.com
www.perishednations.com
www.evolutiondocumentary.com
www.islamdenouncesterrorism.com
www.islamdenouncesantisemitism.com